THE THEORY OF NUMBERS

THE THEORY
OF NUMBERS

NEAL H. McCOY

Gates Professor of Mathematics, Smith College

The Macmillan Company, New York
Collier-Macmillan Limited, London

Third Printing, 1968

Library of Congress catalog card number: 65-16557

THE MACMILLAN COMPANY, NEW YORK
COLLIER-MACMILLAN CANADA, LTD., TORONTO, ONTARIO

PRINTED IN THE UNITED STATES OF AMERICA

Preface

This little book has been designed as a text for a one-semester introductory course at the undergraduate level.

It is assumed that the student has already studied, or is willing to
take on faith, a few of the simple properties of the system of integers.
As examples, the division algorithm is stated without proof, and it is
assumed that every nonempty set of positive integers has a least element. Moreover, proofs by mathematical induction are used without
apology or explanation. Otherwise, the book is essentially self-con-
tained except that elementary properties of limit of a sequence necessarily play an important role in the treatment of infinite continued
fractions in the latter part of the final chapter. Occasional remarks are
addressed to the reader with some knowledge of abstract algebra, but
these may be omitted without any effect upon the understanding of
later text material.

An examination of the table of contents will reveal the scope of the
book. Although no two instructors would likely choose exactly the
same topics for an introductory course in the theory of numbers, it

seems likely that there would be general agreement on the importance of most of the topics here presented. Suggestions of additional topics, with references, are given at the end of each chapter. Some of the topics are natural extensions or generalizations of the material of that particular chapter; others have no direct relation to that material but may be used as desired to modify or enrich the course.

Although the theory of numbers has a most interesting and illuminating history, none of that history has been included in this book. It is my feeling that students should be encouraged to read such material on their own rather than including it as a formal part of an introductory course. In addition to Dickson's classic *History of the Theory of Numbers*, we may mention the excellent book by Ore and, at a more advanced level, that by Shanks. These, as well as a number of other sources, will be found in our list of references.

It would be impossible to mention all of the texts on the theory of numbers to which I am indebted in a conscious or unconscious way. However, I would like to mention specifically the excellent book by Niven and Zuckerman which has been of particular influence in my treatment of certain parts of the theory of continued fractions.

Finally, I wish to express my appreciation to Professor David G. Cantor who read the entire manuscript and made several suggestions for improving the exposition.

Neal H. McCoy

Contents

APPENDIX

INDEX

DIVISORS AND
PRIME NUMBERS

Since we shall be almost entirely concerned with *integers*, it will sometimes be convenient to have available a symbol for the set of all integers (positive, negative, and zero). Accordingly, we shall let I denote this set and, whenever convenient, we shall write $a \in I$ to indicate that a is an element of the set I, that is, that a is an integer. However, let us agree that letters which the context indicates are being used to represent numbers always represent arbitrary integers unless otherwise explicitly stated.

It is clear that what constitutes a proof of some fairly "obvious" property of the integers must depend upon the postulates which are taken as the definition of the system of integers. We shall not start here with such a list of postulates; instead, we assume that the reader has already had some introduction to this subject or is simply willing to accept without proof certain simple properties of the integers which will be stated from time to time, especially in this first chapter. In particular, we assume that the reader has some familiarity with the method of proof by induction.

1.1   DIVISORS AND THE DIVISION ALGORITHM

Let us begin with the following definition.

1.1   DEFINITION. If $a, d \in I$ with $d \neq 0$, we say that d is a *divisor* (or *factor*) of a if there exists $a_1 \in I$ such that $a = a_1 d$. In this case, we say also that d *divides* a or that a is *divisible by* d or that a is a *multiple* of d.

We shall often write $d \mid a$ to indicate that d divides a. Occasionally, $d \nmid a$ may be used to indicate that d does not divide a.

It should be observed that by the above definition, a divisor is always different from zero. If, for example, we write $e \mid f$, it is to be understood that $e \neq 0$ and that the integer e is a divisor of the integer f.

We now state, without proof, a number of simple facts involving the concept of divisor. The reader should verify each of them.

1.2

(i)   *If $d \mid a$ and $a \mid b$, then $d \mid b$.*

(ii)   *$d \mid a$ if and only if $d \mid (-a)$.*

(iii) *$d \mid a$ if and only if $(-d) \mid a$.*

(iv)   *$\pm 1 \mid a$ for every integer a.*

(v)   *If $d \mid \pm 1$, then $d = \pm 1$.*

(vi)   *$d \mid 0$ for every $d \neq 0$.*

(vii) *If $a \mid b$ and $b \mid a$, then $a = \pm b$.*

(viii) *If $a \neq 0$ and $d \mid a$, then $|d| \leq |a|$. Moreover, if $d \mid a$ and $d \neq \pm a$, then $|d| < |a|$.*

(ix)   *If $d \mid a$ and $d \mid b$, then $d \mid (ax + by)$ for arbitrary integers x and y.*

In studying divisibility properties of the integers, we shall sometimes limit ourselves to a consideration of *positive* divisors of *positive* integers. This causes no real loss of generality in view of 1.2 (ii) and (iii).

As special cases of 1.2 (ix) of particular interest, we see that if $d \mid a$ and $d \mid b$, then $d \mid (a + b)$ and $d \mid (a - b)$. Another useful formulation of this result is as follows. If $r + s = t$ and d divides any two of the integers r, s, and t, it also divides the third.

We next state, again without proof, a simple fact which plays a most important role in the study of the integers.

1.3   DIVISION ALGORITHM. If a and b are integers with $b > 0$, there exist *unique* integers q and r such that

1.4 $$a = qb + r, \qquad 0 \leq r < b.$$

We may emphasize that as here formulated a is an arbitrary integer and b is a *positive* integer. The integer q is called the *quotient* and r the *remainder* in the division of a by b. It is clear that b is a divisor of a if and only if the remainder in the division of a by b is zero.

If both a and b are given positive integers, the quotient and the remainder in the division of a by b may be computed by the familiar long division process of arithmetic.

1.2 DIFFERENT BASES

The number 10 is the base in our familiar decimal notation. Thus, for example, 3427 represents the number $3 \cdot 10^3 + 4 \cdot 10^2 + 2 \cdot 10 + 7$. In a similar way, any positive integer $b > 1$ can be used as a base. By this statement, we mean to imply the truth of the following theorem.

1.5 THEOREM. *Let b be a positive integer greater than* 1. *Then every positive integer a can be expressed uniquely in the form*

$$1.6 \qquad a = r_m b^m + r_{m-1} b^{m-1} + \cdots + r_1 b + r_0,$$

where m is a nonnegative integer and the r's are integers such that

$$0 < r_m < b \text{ and } 0 \le r_i < b \text{ for } i = 0, 1, \ldots, m - 1.$$

If 1.6 holds, let us say that the right side of 1.6 is "a representation of a, using the base b." We first sketch a proof that every positive integer has such a representation, and establish the uniqueness a little later.

If $a < b$, then 1.6 holds with $m = 0$ and $r_0 = a$; hence every $a < b$ has a representation, using the base b. Suppose, now, that $a \ge b$ and as an induction hypothesis let us assume that every positive integer less than a has a representation, using the base b. By the division algorithm, we have that

$$1.7 \qquad a = qb + r, \qquad\qquad 0 \le r < b,$$

with $q > 0$ since $a \ge b$, and clearly $q < a$. Therefore, by the induction hypothesis, q has a representation, using the base b. If we substitute this representation for q in 1.7, we immediately obtain a representation of a, using the base b. We have thus established the fact that every positive integer a has such a representation.

Let us now establish the uniqueness of the representation of a, using the base b. If $a < b$, the representation 1.6 must reduce to $a = r_0$ and it is clear that there is no other representation. Accordingly, let us suppose that $a \geq b$ and as an induction hypothesis let us now assume that every positive integer less than a has a *unique* representation, using the base b. If 1.6 holds, then

$$a = (r_m b^{m-1} + \cdots + r_1)b + r_0,$$

and since $0 \leq r_0 < b$, we see that r_0 is the remainder and that $r_m b^{m-1} + \cdots + r_1$ is the quotient in the division of a by b. Moreover, the quotient is greater than zero since $a \geq b$. Suppose, now, that in addition to 1.6 we have the following representation of a, using the base b:

$$a = s_n b^n + \cdots + s_1 b + s_0.$$

Then, by the same argument as applied above to 1.6, we see that s_0 is the remainder and $s_n b^{n-1} + \cdots + s_1$ is the quotient in the division of a by b. However, in the division algorithm the remainder and the quotient are unique. Hence $r_0 = s_0$; also we conclude that

$$r_m b^{m-1} + \cdots + r_1 = s_n b^{n-1} + \cdots + s_1,$$

and the two sides of this equation give representations, using the base b, of a positive number less than a. By our induction hypothesis, we conclude that they are identical, and since we already know that $r_0 = s_0$, we have that $m = n$ and $r_i = s_i$ $(i = 0, 1, \ldots, m)$. This establishes the uniqueness of the representation of a, using the base b, and the proof of the theorem is completed.

Just as we usually omit the powers of 10 in the ordinary decimal notation, we may do likewise when using a base other than 10, provided we make it clear what base is intended. To indicate that 1.6 holds, let us write $a = (r_m r_{m-1} \cdots r_0)_b$. If no base is indicated by a subscript, it is to be understood that the base is 10. For example, since $346 = 2 \cdot 5^3 + 3 \cdot 5^2 + 4 \cdot 5 + 1$, we may write $346 = (2341)_5$.

The proof of the uniqueness part of the above theorem suggests an easy way to obtain the representation of a given number a, using a given base b. It is only necessary to compute the remainders in successive divisions by b. Let us exhibit the calculations for 346, using the base 5. The remainders are written to the right and the divisions are carried out until the last quotient is less than 5. These calculations show that $346 = (2341)_5$, in agreement with what was exhibited above.

$$\begin{array}{r|l}
5 & 346 \\
\hline
5 & 69 \quad\; 1 \\
\hline
5 & 13 \quad\; 4 \\
\hline
& 2 \qquad 3
\end{array}$$

It is possible to perform all the usual operations of arithmetic, using a fixed base other than 10. As examples, the reader may verify the following addition and multiplication, using the base 5.

$$(3314)_5 \qquad\qquad (3214)_5$$
$$(3212)_5 \qquad\qquad (23)_5$$

$$\overline{} \qquad\qquad \overline{}$$

$$(12031)_5 \qquad\qquad (20202)_5$$
$$\qquad\qquad\qquad (11433)_5$$

$$\qquad\qquad\qquad \overline{}$$

$$\qquad\qquad\qquad (140032)_5$$

$$\textit{Addition} \qquad\qquad \textit{Multiplication}$$

In the special case in which the base is 2, the only possible "digits" are 0 and 1. This base is widely used in high-speed computers since, for example, the simple twofold choice of a 0 or a 1 can be indicated by the presence or absence of an electrical current flowing in a given circuit.

Exercises

1.   Let b and m be positive integers. If q is the quotient and r is the remainder when a is divided by b, show that q is the quotient and mr is the remainder when ma is divided by mb.

2.   Let a, b, and c be integers with $b > 0$ and $c > 0$. If q is the quotient when a is divided by b and q' is the quotient when q is divided by c, show that q' is the quotient when a is divided by bc.

3.   Suppose that $n \geq 2$ and that x_i $(i = 1, 2, \ldots, n)$ are given integers. Show that if $\sum_{i=1}^{n} x_i = 0$ and d divides any $n - 1$ of the x_i, it divides all n of them.

4.   Find the representation of each of the following numbers, using the base 7 and also using the base 2:

$$26,\ 14,\ 135,\ 1428,\ 76,\ (312)_5,\ (1321)_4.$$

5.   Carry out the following additions, using the indicated base.

$$(1432)_5 \qquad (71323)_8 \qquad (1011011)_2 \qquad (41356)_7$$
$$(3124)_5 \qquad (3426)_8 \qquad (111001)_2 \qquad (24131)_7$$

$$\overline{} \qquad \overline{} \qquad \overline{} \qquad \overline{}$$

6.   Carry out the following multiplications, using the indicated base.

$$(3124)_5 \qquad (10111)_2 \qquad (4632)_7$$
$$(232)_5 \qquad (1101)_2 \qquad (234)_7$$

$$\overline{} \qquad \overline{} \qquad \overline{}$$

7.   Show that a positive integer is divisible by 8 if and only if the number formed by its last three digits (using the base 10) is divisible by 8.

8.   Find a positive integer n such that every digit of $7n$ (using the base 10) is 9.

1.3   THE GREATEST COMMON DIVISOR OF TWO INTEGERS

We next make the following definition.

1.8   DEFINITION. If a and b are integers, not both of which are zero, the *greatest common divisor* (g.c.d.) of a and b is the unique *positive* integer d with the following two properties:

(i) $d \mid a$ and $d \mid b$.

(ii)   If $c \mid a$ and $c \mid b$, then $c \mid d$.

We shall presently establish the existence of the g.c.d. of any two integers, not both of which are zero. However, we may point out now that there cannot be two different positive integers having the stated properties. For if positive integers d and d_1 have these two properties, it follows that $d \mid d_1$ and $d_1 \mid d$, and hence that $d = d_1$.

It is apparent from the above definition that the g.c.d. of a and b is in fact (as its name suggests) the largest integer which is a divisor of both a and b. However, this fact is not nearly so important as the properties listed in the definition.

In the future, we shall often denote the g.c.d. of a and b by (a, b). Moreover, if e and f are integers and we use the symbol (e, f), it is to be understood (even if not explicitly mentioned) that at least one of these integers is different from zero.

If $b \mid a$, it is easy to verify that $|b|$ satisfies the requirements for the g.c.d. of a and b. Thus we have the following fact.

1.9   *If $b \mid a$, then $(a, b) = |b|$.*

In particular, this says that if $b \neq 0$, then $(0, b) = |b|$.

In view of 1.2 (ii) and (iii), it is clear that we always have

$$(a, b) = (-a, b) = (a, -b) = (-a, -b).$$

Since the case in which either a or b is zero is essentially trivial, we see that in discussing the g.c.d. of two integers there is no real loss of generality in assuming that they are both *positive*. We shall sometimes find it convenient to make this assumption.

Suppose, now, that a and b are nonzero integers and that b at least is positive. We may apply the division algorithm (1.3) and write

$$a = qb + r, \qquad\qquad 0 \leq r < b.$$

If $r = 0$, we have at once from 1.9 that $(a, b) = b$, so we assume henceforth that $r \neq 0$. We next apply the division algorithm to the integers b and r, and obtain

$$b = q_1 r + r_1, \qquad\qquad 0 \leq r_1 < r.$$

By a continuation of this procedure, known as the *Euclidean algorithm*, we obtain a system of equations as follows:

$$a = qb + r, \qquad\qquad 0 < r < b,$$
$$b = q_1 r + r_1, \qquad\qquad 0 < r_1 < r,$$
$$r = q_2 r_1 + r_2, \qquad\qquad 0 < r_2 < r_1,$$

1.10 ....

$$r_{k-2} = q_k r_{k-1} + r_k, \qquad\qquad 0 < r_k < r_{k-1},$$
$$r_{k-1} = q_{k+1} r_k.$$

Since $r > r_1 > r_2 > \cdots$, we must eventually have a zero remainder, and our notation is so chosen that r_k is the last nonzero remainder. We shall now prove the following statement which will establish the existence of the g.c.d. of a and b.

1.11 *In the notation of Equations 1.10 we have $(a, b) = r_k$.*

Now r_k is a positive integer, so we have only to verify the two properties of Definition 1.8. From the last of Equations 1.10, we see that $r_k | r_{k-1}$. Then 1.2 (ix) and the next to the last of these equations shows that $r_k | r_{k-2}$. The preceding equation then shows that $r_k | r_{k-3}$, and continuing up the list of equations we finally obtain that $r_k | b$ and $r_k | a$. Hence r_k satisfies Definition 1.8 (i). Next, suppose that $c | a$ and $c | b$. The first of Equations 1.10 then shows that $c | r$. The next equation then shows that $c | r_1$. Going on down the list of equations, we find eventually that $c | r_k$, and thus r_k satisfies the second property of Definition 1.8, and the proof is completed.

We shall now prove a theorem which will play an important role in the sequel.

1.12 THEOREM. *Let a and b be integers, not both of which are zero, and let $d = (a, b)$. Then there exist integers x and y such that*

$$d = ax + by.$$

Proof: The conclusion is trivial if either a or b is zero since, in this case 1.9 asserts that either $(a, b) = |a|$ or $(a, b) = |b|$. Moreover, we may just as well assume that $b > 0$ since $(a, b) = (a, -b)$ and $(-b)(-y) = by$, so that the desired result holds for $b < 0$ if it holds for $b > 0$.

For convenience, let us define the set S as follows:

$$S = \{ax + by; x,y \in I\}.$$

To prove the theorem we therefore need to show that $d \in S$. We begin by pointing out a few simple properties of the set S.

Since $a = a \cdot 1 + b \cdot 0$, we see that $a \in S$; and in like manner we have $b \in S$. If $u \in S$, clearly $ut \in S$ for each integer t. Moreover, if $u_1, u_2 \in S$, so that $u_1 = ax_1 + by_1$ and $u_2 = ax_2 + by_2$, we see that $u_1 \pm u_2 = a(x_1 \pm x_2) + b(y_1 \pm y_2)$ is also an element of S. In other words, we have verified that the set S contains the integers a and b, and also that it is closed with respect to addition and subtraction, and with respect to multiplication by an arbitrary integer. In particular, if e, f, g, and h are integers such that

$$e = fg + h,$$

and if $e,g \in S$, then $h \in S$. We now apply this result in turn to Equations 1.10. Since $a,b \in S$, the first equation shows that $r \in S$. Now since $b,r \in S$, the second equation shows that $r_1 \in S$. Continuing this process, we see that every remainder is an element of S. Since $r_k = d$, this completes the proof.

It is sometimes convenient to say that the elements of S are the *linear combinations* of a and b. In this language, the theorem just proved states that the g.c.d. of a and b is expressible as a linear combination of a and b.

The method of the above proof can actually be used in a numerical case to express the g.c.d. of two integers as a linear combination of those integers. For example, let $a = 710$ and $b = 68$. The Euclidean algorithm gives us the following system of equations:

$$710 = 10 \cdot 68 + 30,$$
$$68 = 2 \cdot 30 + 8,$$
$$30 = 3 \cdot 8 + 6,$$
$$8 = 1 \cdot 6 + 2,$$
$$6 = 3 \cdot 2.$$

From these equations, we have that $(710, 68) = 2$. Let us now express, in turn, the successive remainders as linear combinations of 710 and 68. For convenience, we shall write a for 710, and b for 68. From the first equation, we have

$$30 = a - 10b.$$

The second equation then gives us

$$
\begin{aligned}
8 &= b - 2 \cdot 30 \\
&= b - 2(a - 10b) \\
&= 21b - 2a.
\end{aligned}
$$

Next, we obtain

$$
\begin{aligned}
6 &= 30 - 3 \cdot 8 \\
&= (a - 10b) - 3(21b - 2a) \\
&= 7a - 73b.
\end{aligned}
$$

Finally, we obtain

$$
\begin{aligned}
2 &= 8 - 6 \\
&= (21b - 2a) - (7a - 73b) \\
&= 94b - 9a.
\end{aligned}
$$

Accordingly, we have shown that

$$2 = 710 \cdot (-9) + 68 \cdot 94.$$

We may point out that in the Euclidean algorithm the restriction on the magnitude of the remainders in Equations 1.10 plays no role except to assure us that we eventually get a zero remainder. In a numerical case, it will sometimes shorten the work to let the remainder be negative. For example, the last three of the above equations giving the Euclidean algorithm for 710 and 68 could be replaced by the following two equations:

$$30 = 4 \cdot 8 - 2,$$
$$8 = 4 \cdot 2.$$

We shall presently obtain several consequences of the last theorem, but first we make the following definition.

1.13   DEFINITION. Integers a and b, not both of which are zero, are said to be *relatively prime* if and only if $(a, b) = 1$. If a and b are relatively prime, we may say also that either of these integers is *relatively prime to* the other.

1.14   COROLLARY. *The integers a and b, not both zero, are relatively prime if and only if there exist integers x and y such that*

1.15 $$1 = ax + by.$$

If $(a, b) = 1$, the existence of x and y satisfying 1.15 is asserted by Theorem 1.12. Conversely, if $d = (a, b)$ and Equation 1.15 holds, 1.2 (ix) shows that $d \mid 1$ and hence (since d is positive) that $d = 1$.

Of course, Equation 1.15 may be interpreted not only as expressing 1 as a linear combination of a and b but also as a linear combination of a and y, or of x and b, or of x and y. Accordingly, Corollary 1.14 establishes the following result.

1.16   *If $1 = ax + by$, then $(a, b) = (a, y) = (x, b) = (x, y) = 1$.*

We next prove the following corollary.

1.17   COROLLARY. *If a and b are nonzero integers and $(a, b) = d$, then $(a/d, b/d) = 1$.*

To see this, let $a = a_1 d$ and $b = b_1 d$, and let us show that $(a_1, b_1) = 1$. By Theorem 1.12, there exist integers x and y such that $d = ax + by$. Thus $d = (a_1 d)x + (b_1 d)y$ and $1 = a_1 x + b_1 y$. Corollary 1.14 then shows that $(a_1, b_1) = 1$, and the proof is completed.

1.18   COROLLARY. *If a, m, and n are nonzero integers, then $(a, mn) = 1$ if and only if $(a, m) = 1$ and $(a, n) = 1$.*

Otherwise expressed, this corollary states that a is relatively prime to mn if and only if it is relatively prime to both m and n. To prove this corollary, suppose first that $(a, mn) = 1$. Then Corollary 1.14 states that $1 = ax + mny$ for certain integers x and y. However, this same equation shows that 1 is expressible as a linear combination of a and m, and it follows that $(a, m) = 1$. Similarly, $(a, n) = 1$. Suppose, next, that $(a, m) = 1$ and $(a, n) = 1$. Then there exist integers r, s, u, and v such that $1 = ar + ms$ and $1 = au + nv$. It follows that

$$1 = ar + ms(au + nv),$$

or

$$1 = a(r + msu) + (mn)(sv),$$

and this equation shows that $(a, mn) = 1$. The proof is therefore completed.

The following result also is an easy consequence of Corollary 1.14.

1.19   COROLLARY. *If a is a nonzero integer such that $a \mid bc$ and $(a, b) = 1$, then $a \mid c$.*

Since $(a, b) = 1$, there exists an equation of the form $1 = ax + by$. Multiplying by c, we obtain the equation

$$c = acx + bcy.$$

It is given that $a \mid bc$, and clearly $a \mid acx$. Hence a divides the right side of this equation and therefore $a \mid c$, as we wished to show.

1.4   THE EQUATION $ax + by = n$

We now change our point of view as follows. Suppose that a, b, and n are given integers, and let us consider an equation of the form

$$ax + by = n,$$

where x and y are restricted to be integers. By a *solution* of this equation we mean, of course, a pair of *integers* x and y which satisfy the equation. It is natural to inquire whether such an equation has a solution, and if it does have a solution whether we can determine all solutions. These questions are settled in the following theorem.

1.20   THEOREM. *Let a, b, and n be given integers with a and b not both zero, and let $(a, b) = d$. Then the equation*

1.21 $$ax + by = n$$

has a solution if and only if $d \mid n$. If $d \mid n$ and x_0, y_0 is one solution of Equation 1.21, then x, y is a solution if and only if

1.22 $$x = x_0 + (b/d)t, \quad y = y_0 - (a/d)t,$$

where t is an integer.

Proof: The reader may verify that the result is trivial if either a or b is zero. Accordingly, we henceforth assume that $a \neq 0$ and $b \neq 0$.

It is clear that if Equation 1.21 holds for integers x and y, then d

divides the left side of the equation and therefore $d \mid n$. Conversely, suppose that $d \mid n$, $n = n_1 d$. By Theorem 1.12, there exist integers r and s such that $d = ar + bs$. Hence $n = n_1 d = a(n_1 r) + b(n_1 s)$, and this completes the proof of the first statement of the theorem. We may remark that this result shows that the set S introduced in the proof of Theorem 1.12 consists of all multiples of d. Incidentally, the *proof* of Theorem 1.12 (using the Euclidean algorithm) furnishes a computational procedure for calculating a solution of Equation 1.21 if a and b are given nonzero integers such that $d \mid n$.

Let us now assume that $d \mid n$ and that x_0, y_0 is one solution of Equation 1.21, and let x, y be any solution. Then $n = ax + by = ax_0 + by_0$, and it follows that

$$a(x - x_0) = b(y_0 - y).$$

If we set $a = a_1 d$ and $b = b_1 d$ and divide the preceding equation by d, we obtain

1.23 $$a_1(x - x_0) = b_1(y_0 - y).$$

Now $(a_1, b_1) = 1$ by Corollary 1.17, and then Corollary 1.19 shows that $b_1 \mid (x - x_0)$, that is, that $x - x_0 = b_1 t$ for some integer t. Substituting in Equation 1.23, we obtain

$$a_1 b_1 t = b_1(y_0 - y),$$

from which it follows that $y_0 - y = a_1 t$. We have therefore shown that $x = x_0 + b_1 t$, $y = y_0 - a_1 t$, for some integer t, and hence that every solution is of the form 1.22. The proof is completed by observing as follows that 1.22 actually gives a solution for *every* integer t:

$$a[x_0 + (b/d)t] + b[y_0 - (a/d)t] = ax_0 + by_0 = n.$$

As a numerical example, let us consider the equation

$$710x + 68y = 6.$$

We showed above, as an illustration of the Euclidean algorithm, that $(710, 68) = 2$ and that

$$710 \cdot (-9) + 68 \cdot 94 = 2.$$

Hence

$$710 \cdot (-27) + 68 \cdot 282 = 6.$$

Using $x_0 = -27$ and $y_0 = 282$ in Equations 1.22, we find that the solutions of our given equation are of the form

$$x = -27 + 34t, \quad y = 282 - 355t, \qquad t \in I.$$

An equation of the type considered in this section is often called a linear indeterminate equation (indeterminate, since there is not a unique solution) or a linear Diophantine equation. This latter name comes from Diophantus of Alexandria, who initiated the study of such equations (of degree higher than the first). One particular Diophantine equation of the second degree will be studied in detail in Chapter V, and references to Diophantine equations will appear at the end of this chapter and at the end of Chapters IV and V.

1.5 THE G.C.D. OF MORE THAN TWO INTEGERS

So far we have considered the greatest common divisor of two integers, but it is fairly easy to extend the concept to more than two integers. In this brief section we give the appropriate definitions and state, for the most part with only hints of proofs, the fundamental properties. Detailed proofs by mathematical induction are not hard to supply and will be left as exercises.

1.24 DEFINITION. The g.c.d. of $k \geq 2$ integers a_i $(i = 1, 2, \ldots, k)$, not all of which are zero, is the unique positive integer d with the following two properties:

(i) $d \mid a_i$ $(i = 1, 2, \ldots, k)$.

(ii) If $c \mid a_i$ $(i = 1, 2, \ldots, k)$, then $c \mid d$.

The g.c.d. of the integers a_i $(i = 1, 2, \ldots, k)$ may be denoted by $(a_1, a_2, \ldots, a_k)$.

If certain of the integers a_i $(i = 1, 2, \ldots, k)$ are zero, clearly $(a_1, a_2, \ldots, a_k)$ coincides with the g.c.d. of the nonzero integers among the a_i. The following result therefore establishes the existence of the g.c.d. of any k integers and also suggests a procedure for computing it.

1.25 Let a_i $(i = 1, 2, \ldots, k)$ be nonzero integers, with $k > 2$. Then

$$(a_1, a_2, \ldots, a_k) = ((a_1, a_2, \ldots, a_{k-1}), a_k).$$

Thus, for example, $(a_1, a_2, a_3) = ((a_1, a_2), a_3)$, since the common divisors of a_1 and a_2 are precisely the divisors of (a_1, a_2). Hence the g.c.d. of any three nonzero integers exists and can be computed by twice computing the g.c.d. of two integers by use of the Euclidean algorithm.

1.26 THEOREM. *If* $d = (a_1, a_2, \ldots, a_k)$, *there exist integers* x_i ($i = 1, 2, \ldots, k$) *such that*

$$d = \sum_{i=1}^{k} a_i x_i.$$

Let us verify this result for the case of *three* nonzero integers. By Theorem 1.12, there exist integers x and y such that

$$(a_1, a_2) = a_1 x + a_2 y.$$

Again applying Theorem 1.12, there exist integers r and s such that

$$((a_1, a_2), a_3) = (a_1, a_2)r + a_3 s.$$

Hence

$$
\begin{aligned}
(a_1, a_2, a_3) &= ((a_1, a_2), a_3) \\
&= (a_1, a_2)r + a_3 s \\
&= (a_1 x + a_2 y)r + a_3 s \\
&= a_1(xr) + a_2(yr) + a_3 s.
\end{aligned}
$$

1.27 DEFINITION. The $k \geq 2$ integers a_i ($i = 1, 2, \ldots, k$), not all of which are zero, are said to be *relatively prime* if and only if $(a_1, a_2, \ldots, a_k) = 1$. They are said to be *relatively prime in pairs* if and only if they are all different from zero and $(a_i, a_j) = 1$ for each $i \neq j$; $i, j = 1, 2, \ldots, k$.

The distinction between these concepts may be emphasized by observing that the three integers 2, 3, and 4 are relatively prime since $(2, 3, 4) = 1$. However, they are not relatively prime in pairs, since $(2, 4) = 2$.

1.28 COROLLARY. *The* $k \geq 2$ *integers* a_i ($i = 1, 2, \ldots, k$), *not all of which are zero, are relatively prime if and only if there exist integers* x_i ($i = 1, 2, \ldots, k$) *such that*

$$1 = \sum_{i=1}^{k} a_i x_i.$$

1.29   COROLLARY. *If $d = (a_1, a_2, \ldots, a_k)$ and we set $a_i = a_i'd$ $(i = 1,$*
$2, \ldots, k)$ then $(a_1', a_2', \ldots, a_n') = 1$.

1.6   THE LEAST COMMON MULTIPLE

In this section we shall present very briefly the concept of least common multiple.

1.30   DEFINITION. The *least common multiple* (l.c.m.) of the nonzero integers a and b is the unique *positive* integer m with the following two properties:

(i) $a \mid m$ and $b \mid m$.

(ii)   If $a \mid c$ and $b \mid c$, then $m \mid c$.

The l.c.m. of a and b will frequently be denoted by $[a, b]$.

It is clear that there cannot exist two different positive integers having properties (i) and (ii) of the above definition. The existence of the l.c.m. of a and b will be an immediate consequence of the following result.

1.31   *If a and b are nonzero integers, then*

$$[a, b] = \frac{|ab|}{(a, b)}.$$

In proving this statement, we may just as well assume that a and b are both positive (why?). If we set $(a, b) = d$, $a = a_1d$, $b = b_1d$, we wish to show that $[a, b] = a_1b_1d$. Clearly, $a \mid a_1b_1d$ and $b \mid a_1b_1d$, so property (i) of Definition 1.30 is satisfied. To verify property (ii), suppose that $a \mid c$ and $b \mid c$, and let us set $c = c_1a = c_1a_1d$, $c = c_2b = c_2b_1d$. It follows that $c_1a_1d = c_2b_1d$ and therefore that $c_1a_1 = c_2b_1$. Hence $b_1 \mid c_1a_1$ and since $(a_1, b_1) = 1$ by Corollary 1.17, Corollary 1.19 asserts that $b_1 \mid c_1$. If we set $c_1 = kb_1$, we have

$$c = c_1a_1d = kb_1a_1d.$$

Hence, $(a_1b_1d) \mid c$, and property (ii) is also satisfied. The proof is therefore completed.

As in the case of the g.c.d., it is easy to extend the definition of the l.c.m. so that it applies to more than two integers.

1.32   DEFINITION. The l.c.m. of $k \geq 2$ nonzero integers a_i $(i = 1, 2, \ldots, k)$ is the unique positive integer m with the following two properties:

   (i) $a_i | m$ $(i = 1, 2, \ldots, k)$.

   (ii) If $a_i | c$ $(i = 1, 2, \ldots, k)$, then $m | c$.

The l.c.m. of the nonzero integers a_i $(i = 1, 2, \ldots, k)$ may be denoted by $[a_1, a_2, \ldots, a_k]$.

1.33   *Let a_i $(i = 1, 2, \ldots, k)$ be nonzero integers, with $k > 2$. Then*

$$[a_1, a_2, \ldots, a_k] = [[a_1, a_2, \ldots, a_{k-1}], a_k].$$

1.34   *If the $k \geq 2$ nonzero integers a_i $(i = 1, 2, \ldots, k)$ are relatively prime in pairs, then*

$$[a_1, a_2, \ldots, a_k] = |a_1 a_2 \cdots a_k|.$$

We leave the proofs of 1.33 and 1.34 as exercises.

Exercises

1.   Find the g.c.d. of each of the following pairs of integers and express it as a linear combination of the two integers:
(i) 78 and 32,   (ii) 181 and 37,   (iii) 484 and 164,   (iv) 1277 and -14 (v) 1728 and 433,   (vi) 4320 and 633.

2.   Prove that if $(a, b) = 1$ and $c | a$, then $(c, b) = 1$.

3.   If $a = qb + r$, prove that $(a, b) = (b, r)$. Then use this fact to show that, in the notation of 1.10, $(a, b) = (r_{k-1}, r_k) = r_k$.

4.   If m is a positive integer, prove that $(ma, mb) = m(a, b)$.

5.   Prove by induction the following generalization of Corollary 1.18. For each positive integer $k \geq 2$, if a and n_i $(i = 1, 2, \ldots, k)$ are nonzero integers, then $(a, n_1 n_2 \cdots n_k) = 1$ if and only if $(a, n_i) = 1$ for $i = 1, 2, \ldots, k$.

6.   Prove that if $(a, b) = 1$, then $(ac, b) = (c, b)$.

7.   Find all solutions in integers of each of the following equations:
   (i) $43x + 21y = 3$,   (ii) $3x + 5y = 110$,
   (iii) $51x + 36y = 1$,   (iv) $7x + 13y = 5$,
   (v) $38x + 42y = -2$,   (vi) $51x + 39y = 6$.

8.   Find all solutions in *positive* integers of each of the following equations:
   (i) $6x + 11y = 104$,   (ii) $5x + 6y = 46$,
   (iii) $27x + 4y = 500$,   (iv) $15x - 38y = 100$.

9. Find all solutions in integers of the following pair of simultaneous equations:

$$7x + 23y = 1,$$
$$5x + 2y + 7z = 46.$$

10. Prove 1.25.

11. Prove 1.26.

12. Suppose that $k \geq 2$ and that a_i $(i = 1, 2, \ldots, k)$ are integers, not all of which are zero. If n is an integer, prove that the equation

$$a_1x_1 + a_2x_2 + \cdots + a_kx_k = n$$

has a solution in integers if and only if $(a_1, a_2, \ldots, a_k) | n$.

13. Use 1.25 to find the g.c.d. of the three integers 30, 72, and 140; and then express it as a linear combination of these three integers.

14. Prove 1.33.

15. Prove 1.34.

16. A pile of coconuts was collected by four men, assisted by a monkey. During the night one of the men arose while the others were asleep and divided the nuts into four equal shares, with one nut left over which he gave to the monkey. He hid one share, put the rest of the nuts into a single pile and went back to sleep. In turn, each of the other three men went through exactly the same procedure, and in each case there was always one nut to give to the monkey. In the morning the four men divided the remaining nuts into four equal shares and again had one nut left over for the monkey. What is the smallest number of nuts which could have been in the original pile?

1.7 PRIMES

Throughout the rest of this chapter we shall consider only positive divisors of positive integers. Moreover, unless explicitly stated otherwise, we shall use the word "divisor" to mean "positive divisor." For example, we may say that the only divisors of 6 are 1, 2, 3, and 6.

1.35 DEFINITION. A positive integer $p \neq 1$ is said to be a *prime* if its only divisors are 1 and p. A positive integer, other than 1, is said to be *composite* if it is not a prime.

It will be observed that, according to this definition, the unity 1 is neither prime nor composite. Also, a positive integer n is composite if and only if there exist integers n_1 and n_2 such that $n = n_1n_2$, $1 < n_1 < n$, $1 < n_2 < n$.

The primes less than 1000 are listed in Table 1. The first few are as follows:

$$2, 3, 5, 7, 11, 13, 17, 19, 23, 29, \ldots .$$

Since the only (positive) divisors of a prime p are 1 and p, for each integer a we have either $(a, p) = 1$ or $(a, p) = p$. That is, a is either relatively prime to p or is divisible by p. Accordingly, we shall often find it convenient to write $(a, p) = 1$ to indicate that $p \nmid a$.

Suppose, now, that a and b are integers such that $p \mid ab$, where p is a prime. If $p \nmid a$, then $(a, p) = 1$ and Corollary 1.19 shows that $p \mid b$. Thus a product of two integers is divisible by the prime p if and only if at least one of the two integers is divisible by p. It is easy to extend this result by induction to a product of any finite number of integers. Using the convenient product notation,

$$a_1 a_2 \cdots a_k = \prod_{i=1}^{k} a_i,$$

we may state this general result as follows:

1.36   LEMMA. *Suppose that p is a prime and that k is an arbitrary positive integer. If $a_1, a_2, \ldots, a_k$ are integers such that*

$$p \mid \prod_{i=1}^{k} a_i,$$

then $p \mid a_i$ for at least one i, $1 \leq i \leq k$.

We next verify the following simple fact.

1.37   LEMMA. *Every integer $n > 1$ has a prime factor.*

Let $n > 1$ be a given positive integer, and let us denote by S the set of all divisors of n that are greater than 1. Since $n \in S$, the set S is not empty and it therefore contains a least element p. Now any divisor of p is also a divisor of n and if p were composite, S would contain smaller elements than p. Accordingly, p is a prime and the lemma is established.

The following result is due to Euclid and so has been known for more than 2000 years.

1.38   THEOREM. *The number of primes is infinite.*

This statement means that for each positive integer n, there exist more than n primes. Suppose that $p_1, p_2, \ldots, p_n$ are n given distinct primes and let us set

$$N = 1 + \prod_{i=1}^{n} p_i.$$

By Lemma 1.37, N has a prime factor p. Moreover, no p_i is a factor of N, for otherwise it would follow that $p_i | 1$. Accordingly, the $n + 1$ primes $p_1, p_2, \ldots, p_n, p$ are distinct. The proof of the theorem thus follows easily by an induction process.

There are various simple and useful ways of classifying the primes. In the first place, let us observe that every positive integer is either *even* or *odd*, that is, is respectively of the form $2n$ or $2n + 1$ for some nonnegative integer n. Now $2n$ cannot be prime unless $n = 1$, so every prime except 2 must be odd. In view of the last theorem, the number of odd primes is therefore infinite.

Similarly, if an integer is divided by 3, the remainder is 0, 1, or 2. It follows that every positive integer is of one of the forms

$$3n, 3n + 1, 3n + 2,$$

for some nonnegative integer n. Again, $3n$ cannot be prime unless $n = 1$, and we conclude that every prime except 3 is of the form $3n + 1$ or $3n + 2$. An equivalent, and sometimes more convenient, way of expressing this fact is to say that every prime except 3 is of one of the forms $3n \pm 1$. As special cases of Theorem 1.39, to be presently stated without proof, there exist an infinite number of primes of the form $3n + 1$ and also an infinite number of primes of the form $3n + 2$.

Let us take one further step and point out that every positive integer is of one of the forms

$$4n, 4n + 1, 4n + 2, 4n + 3,$$

for some nonnegative integer n. Clearly, $4n$ is never prime, and $4n + 2 = 2(2n + 1)$ cannot be prime unless $n = 0$. It follows that every odd prime is of the form $4n + 1$ or $4n + 3$. Of course, we may just as well say that every odd prime is of one of the forms $4n \pm 1$. Actually, there exist an infinite number of primes of each of these forms.

We could also classify the primes in terms of the possible remainders when divided by any other fixed positive integer—just as we have here used 2, 3, and 4.

A few special cases of the following theorem of Dirichlet can be proved in an elementary way (see, e.g., Exercise 5 at the end of the following section), but no simple proof of the general result is known, so we here state it without proof. The special case in which $a = 1$ is an immediate consequence of Theorem 1.38.

1.39 THEOREM. *If a and b are positive integers such that $(a, b) = 1$, there exist an infinite number of primes of the form $an + b$, where n is a positive integer.*

1.8   THE FUNDAMENTAL THEOREM AND SOME APPLICATIONS

It is quite easy to show as follows that an integer $a > 1$ is a prime or is expressible as a product of primes. By Lemma 1.37, a has a prime factor p_1, and we therefore have $a = p_1a_1$ for some positive integer a_1. If $a_1 = 1$, a is a prime p_1. If $a_1 > 1$, a_1 has a prime factor p_2 and there exists a positive integer a_2 such that $a_1 = p_2a_2$ and $a = p_1p_2a_2$. If $a_2 = 1$, a is expressed as a product of the primes p_1 and p_2. If $a_2 > 1$, it must have a prime factor p_3 and $a = p_1p_2p_3a_3$. Since $a > a_1 > a_2 > a_3 \cdots$, this process cannot be repeated indefinitely and for some positive integer r we must have $a_r = 1$ and therefore $a = p_1p_2 \cdots p_r$. Of course, these primes p_1, p_2, ..., p_r need not all be distinct.

We have established one part of the following theorem which plays such an important role in the study of the integers that it has often been called the Fundamental Theorem of Arithmetic. Before stating the theorem, let us simplify matters by agreeing that as a matter of language a product may have only one factor. Accordingly, we need not make a separate statement for the case in which a is itself a prime.

1.40   FUNDAMENTAL THEOREM. *Each integer $a > 1$ can be expressed as a product of primes in one and only one way (except for the order of the factors).*

There remains only to prove the *uniqueness* of the representation of an integer as a product of primes. Let us assume that there exists an integer a which can be expressed as a product of primes in two different ways, and seek a contradiction. Suppose, then, that $a = p_1p_2 \cdots p_r$ and that $a = q_1q_2 \cdots q_s$, where the p's and q's are primes and the p's are not identical with the q's. If then we cancel all equal primes from both sides of the equation

$$p_1p_2 \cdots p_r = q_1q_2 \cdots q_s,$$

we obtain an equation which, by a suitable choice of notation, may be written in the form

$$p_1p_2 \cdots p_i = q_1q_2 \cdots q_j,$$

with $i \geq 1$ and $j \geq 1$. It follows that $p_1 \mid q_1q_2 \cdots q_j$ and, by Lemma 1.36, p_1 divides some one of the primes q_1, q_2, ..., q_j. Hence p_1 must be equal to one of these primes in contradiction of the fact that all equal primes have already been canceled. Our assumption that there exists an integer which can be expressed as a product of primes in two different ways has led to a contradiction, and the proof of the theorem is completed.

In expressing a given integer $a > 1$ as a product of primes, it is often useful to adopt a notation which exhibits all the distinct prime factors of a. The preceding theorem assures us that each integer $a > 1$ can be uniquely expressed in the form

$$1.41 \qquad a = p_1^{k_1}p_2^{k_2} \cdots p_r^{k_r},$$

where $p_1, p_2, \ldots, p_r$ are the *distinct* prime factors of a, and $k_i \geq 1$ ($i=1$, $2, \ldots, r$). The right side of Equation 1.41 may be conveniently called the *standard form* of the integer a.

Suppose, now, that $d|a$, where the standard form of a is given by 1.41. Let us set $a = cd$ and assume that $c > 1$ and $d > 1$. If we express c as a product of primes (not necessarily all distinct) and d as a product of primes, and substitute these respective products for c and d in $a = cd$, we obtain an expression of a as a product of primes. In view of the Fundamental Theorem, we must obtain exactly 1.41 if we collect together all equal primes. We have therefore the following simple, but important, result.

1.42   *If the standard form of a is given by* 1.41, *the divisors of a are precisely those integers d of the form*

$$1.43 \qquad d = p_1^{t_1}p_2^{t_2} \cdots p_r^{t_r}, \qquad 0 \leq t_i \leq k_i \ (i = 1, 2, \ldots, r).$$

Clearly, we obtain the divisor 1 of a by taking every $t_i = 0$ in 1.43; also we obtain a itself if $t_i = k_i$ ($i = 1, 2, \ldots, r$). We may point out that 1.43 need not be quite the standard form of d, since some or all of the exponents may be equal to zero.

The g.c.d. and the l.c.m. of positive integers $a > 1$ and $b > 1$ may easily be computed from a knowledge of the standard forms of a and b. For this purpose, it is convenient to vary the notation slightly as follows. Suppose that $p_1, p_2, \ldots, p_t$ are the distinct primes that occur as factors of either a or b. Hence we have

$$1.44 \qquad a = p_1^{m_1}p_2^{m_2} \cdots p_t^{m_t}, \qquad b = p_1^{n_1}p_2^{n_2} \cdots p_t^{n_t},$$

where the m's and the n's may now be zero. However, for each $i = 1$, $2, \ldots, t$, at least one of m_i and n_i is greater than zero. Let us denote by max $\{m_i, n_i\}$ the larger of m_i and n_i, and by min $\{m_i, n_i\}$ the smaller of m_i and n_i. Of course, if $m_i = n_i$, we understand that max $\{m_i, n_i\}$ = min $\{m_i, n_i\} = m_i = n_i$. The following result is then almost immediate.

1.45 *If a and b are given as in 1.44, then*

$$(a, b) = p_1^{\min\{m_1,\, n_1\}} \, p_2^{\min\{m_2,\, n_2\}} \cdots p_t^{\min\{m_t,\, n_t\}},$$

and

$$[a, b] = p_1^{\max\{m_1,\, n_1\}} \, p_2^{\max\{m_2,\, n_2\}} \cdots p_t^{\max\{m_t,\, n_t\}}.$$

We leave it to the reader to verify that 1.31 is an easy consequence of this result.

As a simple example, let $a = 360$ and $b = 378$. Expressing these integers in standard form, we have $360 = 2^3 \cdot 3^2 \cdot 5$ and $126 = 2 \cdot 3^2 \cdot 7$. In such a numerical example we do not need to write down (as in 1.44) the primes which occur with zero exponents, but can immediately apply 1.45 to obtain

$$(360, 126) = 2 \cdot 3^2$$

and

$$[360, 126] = 2^3 \cdot 3^2 \cdot 5 \cdot 7.$$

Let us next find a simple formula for the *number* of divisors of a given positive integer. For example, $360 = 2^3 \cdot 3^2 \cdot 5$, so 1.42 states that the divisors of 360 are those integers of the form $2^{t_1} \cdot 3^{t_2} \cdot 5^{t_3}$ where t_1 takes any one of the four values 0, 1, 2, 3; t_2 takes any one of the three values 0, 1, 2; and t_3 is either 0 or 1. Accordingly, there are $4 \cdot 3 \cdot 2$ choices of t_1, t_2, and t_3; hence there are $4 \cdot 3 \cdot 2 = 24$ divisors of 360. In the general case, there are $k_i + 1$ choices for t_i in 1.43, so we have the following result.

1.46 *If the standard form of a is given by* 1.41, *then the number of divisors of a is*

$$\prod_{i=1}^{r} (k_i + 1).$$

It is also fairly easy to find a formula for the *sum* of all the divisors of a given integer a. The general argument will be clarified by again considering $360 = 2^3 \cdot 3^2 \cdot 5$. It may be verified that the product

$$(1 + 2 + 2^2 + 2^3)(1 + 3 + 3^2)(1 + 5)$$

can be expressed as the sum of 24 terms of which $1 \cdot 1 \cdot 1$, $2 \cdot 1 \cdot 5$, and $2^2 \cdot 3^2 \cdot 5$ are perhaps typical. In fact, the above product is equal to the sum of all integers of the form $2^{t_1} \cdot 3^{t_2} \cdot 5^{t_3}$, with $0 \le t_1 \le 3$, $0 \le t_2 \le 2$, and $0 \leq t_3 \leq 1$, that is, it is equal to the sum of all divisors of 360. Since

$$1 + p + p^2 + \cdots + p^k = \frac{p^{k+1} - 1}{p - 1},$$

the sum of all divisors of 360 is therefore

$$\frac{2^4 - 1}{2 - 1} \cdot \frac{3^3 - 1}{3 - 1} \cdot \frac{5^2 - 1}{5 - 1} = 15 \cdot 13 \cdot 6 = 1170.$$

It is often convenient to use the notation $\sum_{d \mid a}$ for a sum in which d varies over the (positive) divisors of a. Thus, for example, $\sum_{d \mid a} d$ is just the sum of all the divisors of a. We leave to the reader the verification of the following general result which has been illustrated by the above example.

1.47   *If the standard form of a is given by 1.41, then*

$$\sum_{d \mid a} d = \prod_{i=1}^{r} \frac{p_i^{k_i+1} - 1}{p_i - 1}.$$

Exercises

1.   Show that an odd prime of the form $3n + 1$ actually is of the form $6n + 1$.

2.   Prove that every positive integer of the form $3n + 2$ must have a prime factor of the form $3n + 2$.

3.   For each positive integer n show that none of the following $n - 1$ consecutive integers is prime:

$$n! + 2, \; n! + 3, \ldots, n! + n.$$

4.   If p is an odd prime, show that there are unique positive integers x and y such that $p = x^2 - y^2$.

5.   Prove that there exist an infinite number of primes of the form $4n + 3$. [*Hint:* If $p_1, \ldots, p_k$ are primes of this form, not all prime factors of the integer $4(p_1 p_2 \cdots p_k) + 3$ can be of the form $4n + 1$.]

6.   Show that a positive integer $a > 1$ is a perfect square (that is, is the square of an integer) if and only if in the standard form of a all the exponents are even integers.

7.   Show that if b and c are positive integers such that bc is a perfect square and $(b, c) = 1$, then both b and c are perfect squares.

8.   Prove that there do not exist integers a and b such that $a^2 = 2b^2$.

9.   Prove 1.36 by induction.

10.   If the standard form of a is given by 1.41, and t is a positive integer, prove that

$$\sum_{d \mid a} d^t = \prod_{i=1}^{r} \frac{p_i^{t(k_i + 1)} - 1}{p_i^t - 1}.$$

11.   If a, b, and c are three positive integers, verify that

$$[a, b, c] = \frac{abc}{(ab, ac, bc)}.$$

Generalize to the case of n positive integers.

12.   Let f be a function defined on the positive integers with values which are positive integers, that is, $f(a)$ is a positive integer for each positive integer a. Such a function f is called a *multiplicative* function if $f(ab) = f(a) \cdot f(b)$ whenever $(a, b) = 1$. If $\nu(a)$ denotes the number of divisors of a and $\sigma(a)$ the sum of the divisors of a, verify that ν and σ are multiplicative functions.

1.9   THE BRACKET FUNCTION AND BINOMIAL COEFFICIENTS

Let us make the following definition.

1.48   DEFINITION. If x is an arbitrary real number, the largest integer which does not exceed x will be denoted by $[x]$ and called the *integral part* of x. The function which associates with each real number x the integer $[x]$ is often called the *bracket function*.

As examples of the notation here introduced, we have $[5/3] = 1$, $[\sqrt{5}] = 2$, $[-\pi] = -4$, $[7] = 7$. For any real number x, it is clear that $x = [x] + \alpha$, where $0 \leq \alpha < 1$.

If a and b are integers with b at least being positive, and

$$a = qb + r, \qquad\qquad 0 \leq r < b,$$

then

$$a/b = q + r/b, \qquad\qquad 0 \leq r/b < 1,$$

and it follows that $[a/b] = q$. That is, $[a/b]$ is the quotient in the division of a by b. An equivalent statement is that $[a/b]$ is the largest integer k such that $bk \leq a$.

For later use, we state the following fact (see Exercise 2 at end of Section 1.2).

1.49   *If a, b, and c are integers with b > 0 and c > 0, then*

$$[[a/b]/c] = [a/bc].$$

Until further notice, let p be a fixed prime. If $a > 1$ is a given integer, let us denote by $K(a)$ the largest integer t such that $p^t \mid a$. We now proceed to obtain a formula for $K(n!)$, where n is a positive integer.

The multiples of p which occur in the product defining $n!$ are precisely

$$p, 2p, 3p, \ldots, [n/p]p,$$

and hence $K(n!)$ is the number of times p occurs as a factor in the product of these numbers. It follows that

$$K(n!) = [n/p] + K([n/p]!).$$

In this formula, if we replace n by $[n/p]$ and use 1.49, we obtain

$$K([n/p]!) = [n/p^2] + K([n/p^2]!),$$

so that

$$K(n!) = [n/p] + [n/p^2] + K([n/p^2]!).$$

A repetition of this process shows finally that

1.50 $$K(n!) = \sum_{s=1} [n/p^s].$$

Of course, there are only a finite number of nonzero terms in the sum on the right, since $[n/p^s] = 0$ if $p^s > n$.

As an example, let us find the highest power of 3 in 500!. Thus we have $p = 3$, $n = 500$, and the simple calculations are as follows:

$$[500/3] = 166,$$
$$[500/3^2] = [166/3] = 55,$$
$$[500/3^3] = [55/3] = 18,$$
$$[500/3^4] = [18/3] = 6,$$
$$[500/3^5] = [6/3] = 2.$$

The sum of these is 247, so that 3 appears exactly 247 times as a factor in 500!.

We next use Formula 1.50 to establish the following useful fact.

1.51 *Let n and r be positive integers with $1 \leq r < n$. Then*

1.52
$$\frac{n!}{r!(n-r)!}$$

is an integer.

Let us first observe that if x and y are any real numbers, then $[x + y] \geq [x] + [y]$. In particular, we have for each prime p and each positive integer s that

$$[n/p^s] \geq [r/p^s] + [(n-r)/p^s].$$

It follows from 1.50 that $K(n!) \geq K(r!) + K((n-r)!)$, and p occurs at least as many times in the numerator of 1.52 as in the denominator. Since this is true for every prime, it follows that the denominator is a divisor of the numerator, and the proof is completed.

As a matter of fact, if x and y are real numbers and we expand $(x + y)^n$ by the binomial theorem, the number 1.52 is just the coefficient of $x^{n-r}y^r$ in this expansion. That is, if we make the usual agreement that $0! = 1$, we have

1.53
$$(x + y)^n = \sum_{r=0}^{n} \frac{n!}{r!(n-r)!}\, x^{n-r}y^r.$$

This fact also makes it obvious that 1.52 must be an integer. Since

$$\frac{n!}{r!(n-r)!} = \frac{n(n-1)\cdots(n-r+1)}{r!},$$

we have the following immediate consequence of 1.51.

1.54 *For each positive integer r, the product of any r consecutive positive integers is divisible by $r!$.*

Finally, let us make the following simple observation. If p is a prime and $0 < r < p$, then $p!$ is divisible by p, but neither $r!$ nor $(p-r)!$ can be divisible by p. Accordingly, we have the following result.

1.55 *If p is a prime, in the binomial expansion of $(x + y)^p$ all coefficients except those of x^p and y^p are divisible by p.*

Exercises

1. Find the highest power of 7 contained in 500!; in 1200!; in 2000!.
2. Show that 1000! ends with 249 zeros.
3. If r, s, and t are positive integers, show that

$$\frac{(r + s + t)!}{r!\, s!\, t!}$$

is an integer.

4. Let p be a prime and m and n positive integers. Prove that if $p \mid (m^p - n^p)$, then $p^2 \mid (m^p - n^p)$. [Hint: Consider $(m - n)^p$.]
5. Let

$$n = r_m p^m + r_{m-1} p^{m-1} + \cdots + r_0$$

be the representation of the positive integer n, using the prime p as base. Apply 1.50 to show that

$$K(n!) = \frac{n - (r_m + r_{m-1} + \cdots + r_0)}{p - 1}.$$

Additional Topics

1. Applications of use of base two:

   Russian multiplication. Ore,* p. 38.

   The game of Nim. Hardy and Wright, p. 117; Uspensky and Heaslet, p. 16.

   Bachet's problem of weights (also uses base three). Hardy and Wright, p. 115.

2. Mersenne and Fermat numbers. Ore, p. 69; Hardy and Wright, p. 14.
3. Perfect numbers. Ore, p. 91; Uspensky and Heaslet, p. 80; Shanks, portions of Chap. 1.
4. The sequence of primes. Ore, p. 75; Hardy and Wright, Chaps. 1 and 2.
5. More about linear indeterminate equations. Ore, Chaps. 6 and 7; Uspensky and Heaslet, p. 59 and p. 62.
6. Pythagorean triples. Ore, p. 165; Stewart, Chap. 23; Uspensky and Heaslet, p. 37; LeVeque [11], p. 108.
7. Farey sequences. Niven and Zuckerman, Chap. 6; Hardy and Wright, Chap. 3; Rademacher, Chap. 1.

---

*Items in the list of references at the end of this book will usually be identified by name of author only. Whenever we need to distinguish between different books by the same author we shall indicate the number, enclosed in brackets, of the item in the list.

CHAPTER II

FUNDAMENTAL PROPERTIES

OF CONGRUENCE

The concept of congruence plays a most important role in the theory of numbers. In this chapter we present some of its fundamental properties.

2.1   CONGRUENCE AND RESIDUES

We start with the following definition.

2.1   DEFINITION. Let m be a positive integer. If a and b are integers such that $m \mid (a - b)$, we say that "a is congruent to b modulo m" and write $a \equiv b \pmod{m}$. We may indicate that a is not congruent to b modulo m, that is, that $m \nmid (a - b)$, by writing $a \not\equiv b \pmod{m}$.

As a matter of language, we shall call an expression of the form $a \equiv b \pmod{m}$ a *congruence* or a *congruence modulo m*, and we shall also sometimes call m the *modulus* of this congruence.

If we let $b = 0$ in this definition, we see that $a \equiv 0 \pmod{m}$ is merely another way of stating that $m \mid a$.

Since 1 divides every integer, the case in which $m = 1$ is quite trivial and uninteresting. Accordingly, we may just as well think of m as being larger than 1.

It is a most important fact that congruence modulo m is an *equivalence relation* on the set I of all integers. By this statement we mean that it has the following three properties which the reader is asked to verify:

(i) $a \equiv a \pmod{m}$ for each $a \in I$ (*reflexive property*).

(ii) If $a, b \in I$ such that $a \equiv b \pmod{m}$, then
      $b \equiv a \pmod{m}$ (*symmetric property*).

(iii) If $a, b, c \in I$ such that $a \equiv b \pmod{m}$ and
      $b \equiv c \pmod{m}$, then $a \equiv c \pmod{m}$ (*transitive property*).

Some additional terms are introduced in the following definition.

2.2   DEFINITION. If $a \equiv b \pmod{m}$, then b may be said to be a *residue* of a modulo m. For each integer a, let E_a be the set of all residues of a modulo m, that is,

$$E_a = \{x; x \in I, x \equiv a \pmod{m}\}.$$

Such a set E_a is called a *residue class modulo m*.

If b is a residue of a modulo m, the symmetric property of congruence modulo m shows that a is also a residue of b modulo m.

The reader may already be familiar with the concept of *equivalence set* (or *equivalence class*) relative to a given equivalence relation. A residue class modulo m is just a special name for an equivalence set relative to the particular equivalence relation of congruence modulo m defined on the set I. The notation E_a for a residue class modulo m does not exhibit the integer m which is being used as the modulus. Accordingly, whenever there is any danger of confusion, we shall explicitly state what the modulus is.

We now make several observations about residue classes modulo m. Clearly, we always have $a \in E_a$ by the reflexive property of congruence. Moreover, the symmetric and transitive properties show that $E_b = E_a$ if and only if $b \equiv a \pmod{m}$, so that $E_b = E_a$ if and only if $b \in E_a$. We may also point out that if $c, d \in I$, then E_c and E_d have no elements in common unless $c \equiv d \pmod{m}$, in which case $E_c = E_d$.

Since $x \equiv a \pmod{m}$ if and only if there exists an integer y such that $x = a + ym$, the residue class E_a may also be characterized as follows:

$$E_a = \{a + ym; y \in I\}.$$

Moreover, it may be verified that $(a + ym, m) = (a, m)$, and we conclude that all elements of E_a have with m the same greatest common divisor. In particular, *either all elements of E_a are relatively prime to m or no element of E_a is relatively prime to m* (according as $(a, m) = 1$ or $(a, m) > 1$).

By the division algorithm, each integer a can be uniquely expressed in the form $a = qm + r$, where $0 \le r < m$. Since $a \equiv r \pmod{m}$, we have that $E_a = E_r$. Thus E_a consists of all those integers which, when divided by m, have the same remainder as when a is divided by m. Since there are m possible remainders $0, 1, \ldots, m - 1$, every residue class modulo m coincides with one of $E_0, E_1, \ldots, E_{m-1}$. Moreover, these classes are all different (why?), so that every integer is in exactly one of these m residue classes. As an example, suppose for the moment that $m = 5$. Then we see that every integer is in exactly one of the following five residue classes modulo 5:

$$E_0 = \{\ldots, -15, -10, -5, 0, 5, 10, 15, \ldots\},$$

$$E_1 = \{\ldots, -14, -9, -4, 1, 6, 11, 16, \ldots\},$$

$$E_2 = \{\ldots, -13, -8, -3, 2, 7, 12, 17, \ldots\},$$

$$E_3 = \{\ldots, -12, -7, -2, 3, 8, 13, 18, \ldots\},$$

$$E_4 = \{\ldots, -11, -6, -1, 4, 9, 14, 19, \ldots\}.$$

Example. Find (i) the least positive residue of 361 modulo 23, and (ii) the residue of 361 modulo 23 of least absolute value.

Solution: By the division algorithm, we find that $361 = 15 \cdot 23 + 16$, so that $361 \equiv 16 \pmod{23}$ and 16 is the least positive residue of 361 modulo 16. However, $361 \equiv -23 + 16 \equiv -7 \pmod{23}$ and it follows that -7 is the residue of 361 modulo 23 of least absolute value.

We may remark that the least nonnegative residue of a modulo m is always the unique number of the set $\{0, 1, \ldots, m - 1\}$ to which a is congruent modulo m. However, it may happen that there is not a *unique* residue of least absolute value. For example, both 3 and -3 are residues of 9 modulo 6 of least absolute value.

The following concept is frequently useful.

2.3 DEFINITION. A set C of integers is said to be a *complete residue system modulo m* if every integer is congruent modulo m to exactly one integer of the set C.

We have observed above that $\{0, 1, \ldots, m - 1\}$ is a complete residue system modulo m. However, there are many different ways to choose a complete residue system modulo m, since we may choose in an arbitrary way exactly one integer from each of the m different residue classes. For example, each of the following is a complete residue system modulo 5:

$$\{0, 1, 2, 3, 4,\}, \{5, -4, 12, 3, 19\}, \{103, 204, 51, 62, 1000\}.$$

The following simple criterion is sometimes useful in determining whether a given set of integers is a complete residue system modulo m.

2.4 *A set S of integers is a complete residue system modulo m if and only if both of the following conditions are satisfied:*

(i) *S has m elements.*

(ii) *If $s, t \in S$ such that $s \equiv t \pmod{m}$, then $s = t$.*

It is almost obvious that a complete residue system modulo m must satisfy these two conditions. Conversely, suppose that the two conditions are satisfied by a set S. Condition (ii) assures us that the elements of S are *incongruent* modulo m, that is, that no two distinct elements are congruent modulo m. Since, by condition (i), S contains m elements, exactly one element of S is in each of the m different residue classes modulo m. Since every integer is in exactly one of these residue classes, it follows that S is a complete residue system modulo m.

Let us establish several other properties of congruence which will be exceedingly useful in the sequel.

2.5 *If $a \equiv b \pmod{m}$ and $c \equiv d \pmod{m}$, then $a + c \equiv b + d \pmod{m}$ and $ac \equiv bd \pmod{m}$.*

The hypothesis assures us that there exists an integer u such that $a = b + um$ and an integer v such that $c = d + vm$. Hence we have

$$a + c = b + d + (u + v)m$$

and

$$ac = bd + (bv + du + uvm)m,$$

from which the desired conclusions follow.

Remark. If on the set of all residue classes modulo m we define addition and multiplication as follows:

$$E_a + E_b = E_{a+b}, \qquad E_a \cdot E_b = E_{ab},$$

it is the properties established in 2.5 which assure us that addition and multiplication are well-defined (that is, depend only upon the residue classes themselves). With this addition and multiplication, it can be shown that the set of all residue classes modulo m is a ring. This ring, which may be denoted by $I/(m)$, is called the ring of integers modulo m.

Since for each integer c, we have $c \equiv c \pmod{m}$, the following result is a special case of 2.5.

2.6 *If $a \equiv b \pmod{m}$, then $a + c \equiv b + c \pmod{m}$ and $ac \equiv bc \pmod{m}$ for each integer c.*

The properties proved in 2.5 can easily be extended by induction to give the following result.

2.7 *Let k be an arbitrary positive integer and suppose that $a_i \equiv b_i \pmod{m}$ for $i = 1, 2, \ldots, k$. Then*

(i) $$\sum_{i=1}^{k} a_i \equiv \sum_{i=1}^{k} b_i \pmod{m},$$

and

(ii) $$\prod_{i=1}^{k} a_i \equiv \prod_{i=1}^{k} b_i \pmod{m}.$$

If we take $a_i = a$ and $b_i = b$ for $i = 1, 2, \ldots, k$, we obtain the following special case of 2.7 (ii).

2.8 *If $a \equiv b \pmod{m}$, then $a^k \equiv b^k \pmod{m}$ for each positive integer k.*

Using these results, let us now prove the following useful theorem.

2.9 THEOREM. *Let $f(x) = \sum_{k=0}^{n} r_k x^k$ and $g(x) = \sum_{k=0}^{n} s_k x^k$ be polynomials with integral coefficients. If $a \equiv b \pmod{m}$ and $r_k \equiv s_k \pmod{m}$ for each k, then $f(a) \equiv g(b) \pmod{m}$. In particular, $f(a) \equiv f(b) \pmod{m}$.*

PROOF: By 2.8, for each k we have $a^k \equiv b^k \pmod{m}$. Then, by 2.5, it follows that $r_k a^k \equiv s_k b^k \pmod{m}$. Finally, 2.7 (i) then implies that

$$\sum_{k=0}^{n} r_k a^k \equiv \sum_{k=0}^{n} s_k b^k \pmod{m},$$

that is, that $f(a) \equiv g(b) \pmod{m}$. The last statement of the theorem is the special case in which $r_k = s_k$ for $k = 0, 1, \ldots, n$.

If $d \neq 0$, it is clear that $m \,|\, (a - b)$ if and only if $md \,|\, (a - b)d$. Accordingly, we have the following simple result in which we assume that $d > 0$ because we have restricted the modulus to be positive.

2.10 *If $d > 0$, then $a \equiv b \pmod{m}$ if and only if $ad \equiv bd \pmod{md}$.*

In 2.6 we have pointed out that we can add the same integer to both sides of a congruence, or multiply both sides of a congruence by the same integer. Since subtraction of c means adding $-c$, we have a similar result for subtraction which gives the following useful cancellation law.

2.11 *If $a + c \equiv b + c \pmod{m}$, then $a \equiv b \pmod{m}$.*

The situation is different when we come to consider division. However, we may prove the following result.

2.12 *If $ab \equiv ac \pmod{m}$ and $d = (a, m)$, then $b \equiv c \pmod{m/d}$.*

This is easily verified as follows. The hypothesis implies that there exists an integer y such that $ab - ac = ym$ or $a(b - c) = ym$. It follows that $(a/d)(b - c) = y(m/d)$, and we know that a/d and m/d are relatively prime by 1.17. Then 1.19 assures us that m/d divides $b - c$, and this is equivalent to the statement that $b \equiv c \pmod{m/d}$.

A special case of this last result of very frequent use is the following.

2.13 *If $ab \equiv ac \pmod{m}$ and if $(a, m) = 1$, then $b \equiv c \pmod{m}$.*

Otherwise expressed, we can cancel from both sides of a congruence (and without changing the modulus) a common factor which is *relatively prime* to the modulus.

For future reference, let us also state the following result which is an immediate consequence of the definition of the least common multiple.

2.14 *If m_i $(i = 1, 2, \ldots, k)$ are positive integers, then*

$$a \equiv b \pmod{m_i} \qquad\qquad (i = 1, 2, \ldots, k),$$

if and only if

$$a \equiv b \pmod{[m_1, m_2, \ldots, m_k]}.$$

We have now established the most fundamental properties of congruence. The reader should consciously try to develop manipulative skill in using these properties and refer back to the *definition* of congruence only whenever it is necessary to do so.

We conclude this section by proving one further result and then giving several illustrative examples.

2.15   THEOREM. *If C is a complete residue system modulo m and if $(m, n) = 1$, then for each integer r the set*

$$S = \{qn + r; q \in C\}$$

is also a complete residue system modulo m.

PROOF: Suppose that $q_1, q_2 \in C$ such that $q_1n + r \equiv q_2n + r \pmod{m}$. From 2.11, it follows that $q_1n \equiv q_2n \pmod{m}$, and 2.13 then implies that $q_1 \equiv q_2 \pmod{m}$. However, q_1 and q_2 are elements of the **complete** residue system C, so we must have $q_1 = q_2$, and we therefore conclude that $q_1n + r = q_2n + r$. Since C has m elements, it is now clear that S has m incongruent elements and the desired result follows as an immediate consequence of 2.4.

Example 1. Find the remainder in the division of 2^{20} by 7.

Solution: The procedure is to use some of the preceding results to determine, using a minimum of calculation, the least nonnegative residue of 2^{20} modulo 7.

Clearly, $2^3 \equiv 8 \equiv 1 \pmod 7$ and, by 2.8, it follows that $(2^3)^6 \equiv 1^6$ $\pmod 7$ or $2^{18} \equiv 1 \pmod 7$. Multiplying both sides by 2^2 (using 2.6), we find that $2^{20} \equiv 4 \pmod 7$. Hence the desired remainder is 4.

Example 2. Show that $(2^{15})(14^{40}) + 1$ is divisible by 11.

Solution: We begin by finding residues of 2^{15} modulo 11 and of 14^{40} modulo 11 of small absolute value. By simple calculation, we see that $2^4 \equiv 5 \pmod{11}$. Then, using 2.8, we find that $2^8 \equiv 5^2 \equiv 3 \pmod{11}$. By 2.5 we may multiply corresponding sides of this congruence and the preceding one to obtain $2^{12} \equiv 15 \equiv 4 \pmod{11}$. Multiplying both sides by 2^3, we conclude that $2^{15} \equiv 32 \equiv -1 \pmod{11}$.

Since $14 \equiv 3 \pmod{11}$, 2.8 assures us that $14^{40} \equiv 3^{40} \pmod{11}$, so we work with 3^{40}. Our calculations are as follows, with reasons omitted: $3^2 \equiv -2 \pmod{11}$, $3^4 \equiv 4 \pmod{11}$, $3^8 \equiv 16 \equiv 5 \pmod{11}$, $3^{10} \equiv -10$ $\equiv 1 \pmod{11}$, $3^{40} \equiv 1 \pmod{11}$.

Since $2^{15} \equiv -1 \pmod{11}$ and $14^{40} \equiv 1 \pmod{11}$, 2.5 assures us that $(2^{15})(14^{40}) + 1 \equiv (-1)(1) + 1 \equiv 0 \pmod{11}$, and we have the desired result.

Example 3. If $f(x) = 12x^5 - 7x^4 + 8x^2 - 3$, find the least nonnegative residue of $f(18)$ modulo 5.

Solution: By Theorem 2.9, we may consider $f(3)$ instead of $f(18)$, since $18 \equiv 3 \pmod{5}$. Moreover, we may replace each coefficient of $f(x)$ by any other integer to which it is congruent modulo 5. Hence we have

$$f(18) \equiv f(3) \equiv 2 \cdot 3^5 - 2 \cdot 3^4 + 3 \cdot 3^2 - 3 \pmod{5}.$$

Now $3^2 \equiv 4 \pmod{5}$, $3^4 \equiv 16 \equiv 1 \pmod{5}$, and $3^5 \equiv 3 \pmod{5}$. Hence

$$f(18) \equiv 2 \cdot 3 - 2 \cdot 1 + 3 \cdot 4 - 3 \equiv 13 \equiv 3 \pmod{5}.$$

We have thus shown that the least nonnegative residue of $f(18)$ modulo 5 is 3.

Exercises

1. Find the remainder if 3^{40} is divided by 23.

2. Show that $2^{37} - 1$ is divisible by 223.

3. Find the least nonnegative residue of (i) 2^{1000} modulo 15, (ii) $-41{,}260$ modulo 1000, (iii) $16!$ modulo 17, (iv) $2^{10} \cdot 3^{12}$ modulo 11, (v) 3^{5000} modulo 13.

4. Find the smallest positive integer n such that $2^n \equiv 1 \pmod{17}$.

5. Verify that $2^{2^5} + 1$ is divisible by 641.

6. Which of the following are complete residue systems modulo 7: $\{19, 23, 28, 34, 57, 80, -10\}$, $\{0, 10, 10^2, 10^3, 10^4, 10^5, 10^6\}$, $\{99, 14, 237, 25, 353, 929, 13\}$?

7. If m is an odd positive integer, show that $\left\{ -\dfrac{m-1}{2}, \ldots, -2, -1, 0, 1, 2, \ldots, \dfrac{m-1}{2} \right\}$ is a complete residue system modulo m.

8. If $f(x) = 143x^3 + 27x^2 - 4x + 11$, find the least nonnegative residue of (i) $f(2)$ modulo 3, (ii) $f(-2)$ modulo 5, (iii) $f(4)$ modulo 12, (iv) $f(17)$ modulo 11, (v) $f(1000)$ modulo 17.

9. Show that every square number is congruent modulo 4 to either 0 or 1. Use this fact to show that there do not exist integers x and y such that $x^2 + y^2 = 1839$.

10. Prove that $n^7 - n$ is divisible by 42 for every positive integer n.

11. If p is a prime, prove that for arbitrary integers a and b, $(a + b)^p \equiv a^p + b^p \pmod{p}$.

12. If p is a prime, prove by induction that $n^p \equiv n \pmod{p}$ for every positive integer n.

13. Show that a positive integer given in ordinary decimal notation is congruent modulo 9 to the sum of its digits. [Example: $456 \equiv 4 + 5 + 6 \pmod{9}$.]

14. If $(m, n) > 1$, prove that the set S of Theorem 2.15 cannot be a complete residue system modulo m.

15. Let a, u, v, and m be integers, of which at least the last three are positive. If $a^u \equiv 1 \pmod{m}$ and $a^v \equiv 1 \pmod{m}$, prove each of the following:

(i) If r is the remainder when u is divided by v, then $a^r \equiv 1 \pmod{m}$.

(ii) $a^{(u,\ v)} \equiv 1 \pmod{m}$.

2.2 THE ϕ-FUNCTION AND REDUCED RESIDUE SYSTEMS

We introduce in the following definition a universally used notation due to Euler.

2.16 DEFINITION. For each positive integer m, the number of integers in the set $\{1, 2, \ldots, m\}$ which are relatively prime to m is denoted by $\phi(m)$.

For example $\phi(6) = 2$, since only the two integers 1 and 5 in the set $\{1, 2, 3, 4, 5, 6\}$ are relatively prime to 6. We may observe that $\phi(1) = 1$ since $(1, 1) = 1$. Moreover, if $m > 1$, then $(m, m) = m \neq 1$, so that for $m > 1$, $\phi(m)$ is actually the number of positive integers which are *less* than m and relatively prime to m. Near the end of this section we shall obtain a simple formula for $\phi(m)$. However, if p is a prime, it is easy to verify that $\phi(p) = p - 1$, since every positive integer less than p is relatively prime to p.

We showed in the previous section that either all elements of a given residue class modulo m are relatively prime to m, or none of them is relatively prime to m. Now $\{1, 2, \ldots, m\}$ is a complete residue system modulo m, so the following fact is an immediate consequence of Definition 2.16.

2.17 *For each positive integer m, there are precisely $\phi(m)$ different residue classes modulo m whose elements are integers which are relatively prime to m.*

It is evident that every complete residue system modulo m contains $\phi(m)$ integers which are relatively prime to m. Moreover, every integer which is relatively prime to m must be congruent modulo m to exactly one of these integers. Therefore, the set of the $\phi(m)$ integers of a complete residue system modulo m which are relatively prime to m is a reduced residue system modulo m according to the following definition.

2.18 DEFINITION. A set R of integers, each of which is relatively prime to m, is called a *reduced residue system modulo m* if every integer which is relatively prime to m is congruent modulo m to exactly one integer of the set R.

In 2.4, we gave conditions under which a given set of integers is a complete residue system modulo m. An analogous result for reduced residue systems is the following:

2.19 *A set S of integers is a reduced residue system modulo m if and only if the following three conditions are all satisfied:*

(i) $(s, m) = 1$ *for each element s of S.*

(ii)   *S has $\phi(m)$ elements.*

(iii)   *If s, $t \in S$ such that $s \equiv t$ (mod m), then $s = t$.*

Our previous observations show that a reduced residue system must have these three properties. The converse follows easily from the following observations. Conditions (ii) and (iii) state that the elements of S lie in $\phi(m)$ different residue classes; hence exactly one of them must lie in each of the $\phi(m)$ residue classes described in 2.17. Finally, every integer which is relatively prime to m is in one of these residue classes and hence is congruent modulo m to exactly one element of S.

Let us use the result just established to prove the following theorem.

2.20   THEOREM. *If R is a reduced residue system modulo m and if $(a, m) = 1$, then the set*

$$T = \{ar; r \in R\}$$

is a reduced residue system modulo m.

PROOF: Since $(a, m) = 1$ and $(r, m) = 1$ for each $r \in R$, it follows (by 1.18) that $(ar, m) = 1$, and T satisfies the first condition of 2.19. Moreover, T has $\phi(m)$ elements since the reduced residue system R has $\phi(m)$ elements. Finally, suppose that r_1, $r_2 \in R$ such that $ar_1 \equiv ar_2$ (mod m). Since $(a, m) = 1$, this implies that $r_1 \equiv r_2$ (mod m). Then 2.19 (iii), applied to R, asserts that $r_1 = r_2$, and we conclude that $ar_1 = ar_2$. Accordingly, T satisfies all conditions of 2.19, and the proof is completed.

We next establish the following result, which will be useful in the section that follows.

2.21   LEMMA. *If both $\{a_1, a_2, \ldots, a_{\phi(m)}\}$ and $\{b_1, b_2, \ldots, b_{\phi(m)}\}$ are reduced residue systems modulo m, then*

$$\prod_{i=1}^{\phi(m)} a_i \equiv \prod_{i=1}^{\phi(m)} b_i \pmod{m}.$$

PROOF: Each of the a's, being relatively prime to m, must be congruent modulo m to exactly one of the b's. Accordingly, we have a system of congruences

$$a_1 \equiv b_{i_1} \pmod{m},$$

$$a_2 \equiv b_{i_2} \pmod{m},$$

$$\cdots \cdots \cdots \cdots \cdots$$

$$a_{\phi(m)} \equiv b_{i_{\phi(m)}} \pmod{m},$$

where $i_1, i_2, \ldots, i_{\phi(m)}$ are the integers $1, 2, \ldots, \phi(m)$ in some order. The desired result then follows at once from 2.7 (ii).

We next turn to the problem of obtaining a general formula for $\phi(m)$. We pointed out above that if p is a prime, then $\phi(p) = p - 1$. A generalization of this fact is the following:

2.22   LEMMA. *If p is a prime and k an arbitrary positive integer, then*

$$\phi(p^k) = p^k - p^{k-1} = p^{k-1}(p - 1) = p^k(1 - 1/p).$$

PROOF: The integers in the set $\{1, 2, \ldots, p^k\}$ which are *not* relatively prime to p^k are precisely the p^{k-1} integers $p, 2p, \ldots, p^{k-1} \cdot p$ which are divisible by p. Hence there are in the stated set exactly $p^k - p^{k-1}$ integers which are relatively prime to p, and this completes the proof.

The following theorem will be of help in obtaining a formula for $\phi(m)$ if m has more than one prime factor.

2.23   THEOREM. *If R is a reduced residue system modulo m and S is a reduced residue system modulo n, and if $(m, n) = 1$, then*

2.24 $$\{nr + ms; r \in R, s \in S\}$$

is a set of $\phi(m)\phi(n)$ distinct integers which form a reduced residue system modulo mn.

PROOF: It will be an immediate consequence of this theorem that if $(m, n) = 1$, then $\phi(mn) = \phi(m)\phi(n)$. However, we do not as yet know this fact, so we cannot use 2.19 and instead must go back to Definition 2.18 of a reduced residue system.

First, then, let us show that each element $nr + ms$ of the set 2.24 is relatively prime to mn. In view of Corollary 1.18, it is sufficient to prove that it is relatively prime to each of m and n. We have that $nr + ms \equiv nr \pmod{m}$ and $(nr, m) = 1$, since $(n, m) = 1$ and $(r, m) = 1$. Hence $(nr + ms, m) = 1$. Similarly, $(nr + ms, n) = 1$, and therefore $(nr + ms, mn) = 1$, as we wished to show.

Next, let us show that if $r_1, r_2 \in R$ and $s_1, s_2 \in S$ such that

2.25 $$nr_1 + ms_1 \equiv nr_2 + ms_2 \pmod{mn},$$

then $r_1 = r_2$ and $s_1 = s_2$. The congruence 2.25 implies that $nr_1 \equiv nr_2 \pmod{m}$ and, since $(m, n) = 1$, that $r_1 \equiv r_2 \pmod{m}$. But since r_1 and r_2 are elements of a reduced residue system modulo m, we must have $r_1 = r_2$. Similarly, $s_1 = s_2$, and we conclude that a congruence 2.25 holds only if $r_1 = r_2$ and $s_1 = s_2$. Thus, there are $\phi(m)\phi(n)$ incongruent integers in the set 2.24.

There remains only to prove that if $(a, mn) = 1$, then a is congruent modulo mn to an integer of the set 2.24. By Corollary 1.14, there exist integers x and y such that $1 = mx + ny$, and therefore

$$2.26 \qquad\qquad a = amx + any.$$

Now $(x, n) = 1$ and $(y, m) = 1$ (why?); hence we have $(ax, n) = 1$ and $(ay, m) = 1$. It follows that there exist $r \in R$ and $s \in S$ such that $ax \equiv s$ (mod n) and $ay \equiv r$ (mod m). By definition of congruence, there thus exist integers u and v such that $ax = s + un$ and $ay = r + vm$. Substituting in Equation 2.26, we find that

$$a = m(s + un) + n(r + vm)$$
$$= nr + ms + (u + v)mn.$$

Thus $a \equiv nr + ms$ (mod mn), and this completes the proof.

Since, by 2.19, a reduced residue system modulo mn must have $\phi(mn)$ elements, the theorem just proved gives us the following important result.

2.27 **THEOREM.** *If m and n are positive integers such that $(m, n) = 1$, then $\phi(mn) = \phi(m)\phi(n)$.*

Suppose now that $a > 1$ is a given positive integer and that the standard form of a is as follows:

$$a = p_1^{k_1} p_2^{k_2} \cdots p_r^{k_r}.$$

Since $p_1^{k_1}$ is relatively prime to $p_2^{k_2} \cdots p_r^{k_r}$, the preceding theorem shows that

$$\phi(a) = \phi(p_1^{k_1})\phi(p_2^{k_2} \cdots p_r^{k_r}).$$

Continuing this procedure (induction is really involved), we easily obtain

$$\phi(a) = \phi(p_1^{k_1})\phi(p_2^{k_2}) \cdots \phi(p_r^{k_r}).$$

In view of Lemma 2.22, we thus have

$$2.28 \qquad \phi(a) = (p_1^{k_1} - p_1^{k_1-1})(p_2^{k_2} - p_2^{k_2-1}) \cdots (p_r^{k_r} - p_r^{k_r-1}),$$

or

$$2.29 \qquad \phi(a) = p_1^{k_1} p_2^{k_2} \cdots p_r^{k_r} \left(1 - \frac{1}{p_1}\right)\left(1 - \frac{1}{p_2}\right) \cdots \left(1 - \frac{1}{p_r}\right).$$

Using the convenient notation

$$\prod_{p \mid a} \left(1 - \frac{1}{p}\right)$$

for the product of all expressions of the form $1 - \frac{1}{p}$, where p varies over the distinct prime factors of a, Equation 2.29 can be stated in the following elegant way.

2.30   THEOREM. *For each positive integer $a > 1$, we have*

$$\phi(a) = a \prod_{p \mid a} \left(1 - \frac{1}{p}\right).$$

In actually computing $\phi(a)$ for a given integer a, 2.28 is often simpler to use than 2.29 (or the equivalent 2.30). For example, to compute $\phi(90)$, we first express 90 in standard form as follows: $90 = 2 \cdot 3^2 \cdot 5$. Hence, 2.28 gives us at once

$$\phi(90) = (2 - 1)(3^2 - 3)(5 - 1) = 24.$$

We conclude this section by proving the following theorem.

2.31   THEOREM. *For each positive integer a, we have*

$$\sum_{d \mid a} \phi(d) = a.$$

We are here again using $\sum_{d \mid a}$ to indicate a sum in which d varies over the divisors of a. As an illustration of the theorem, we observe that the divisors of 10 are 1, 2, 5, and 10. Hence

$$\sum_{d \mid 10} \phi(d) = \phi(1) + \phi(2) + \phi(5) + \phi(10)$$

$$= 1 + 1 + 4 + 4 = 10.$$

As a first step in proving the theorem, let us prove the following lemma.

2.32   LEMMA. *If $d \mid a$, the number of integers in the set $S = \{1, 2, \ldots, a\}$ which have with a the greatest common divisor d is $\phi(a/d)$.*

The integers in the set S which are divisible by d are precisely the integers in the set

$$T = \{d, 2d, \ldots, a'd\},$$

where $a' = a/d$. But it is obvious from 1.45 (cf. also Exercise 4, page 16) that

$$(kd, a) = (kd, a'd) = d(k, a'),$$

so that $(kd, a) = d$ if and only if $(k, a') = 1$. Therefore the number of integers in the set T, and therefore also in the set S, which have with a the greatest common divisor d is the number of integers in the set $\{1, 2, \ldots, a'\}$ which are relatively prime to a', that is, it is just $\phi(a')$. Since $a' = a/d$, the proof of the lemma is completed.

Now each of the a numbers in the set S has with a the greatest common divisor d for *some* divisor d of a. Accordingly, the lemma shows that we must have

2.33
$$a = \sum_{d \mid a} \phi(a/d).$$

Suppose, now, that the distinct divisors of a are $d_1, d_2, \ldots, d_s$, and let us set

$$a = a_1 d_1 = a_2 d_2 = \cdots = a_s d_s.$$

Then $a_1, a_2, \ldots, a_s$ are s distinct divisors of a, and we must have $\{a_1, a_2, \ldots, a_s\} = \{d_1, d_2, \ldots, d_s\}$. Thus, in particular,

2.34
$$\sum_{i=1}^{s} \phi(a_i) = \sum_{i=1}^{s} \phi(d_i).$$

Moreover, the left side of Equation 2.34 is exactly the right side of Equation 2.33, and the right side of Equation 2.34 is another way of writing

$$\sum_{d \mid a} \phi(d).$$

Therefore,

$$a = \sum_{d \mid a} \phi(d),$$

and this completes the proof of the theorem.

Exercises

1. Compute $\phi(m)$ for $m = 12, 68, 100, 125, 97, 462$, and 1000.

2. If p is an odd prime, show that $\left\{ -\dfrac{p-1}{2}, \ldots, -2, -1, 1, 2, \ldots \right.$ $\left. \dfrac{p-1}{2} \right\}$ is a reduced residue system modulo p.

3. Verify that $\{2, 2^2, 2^3, \ldots, 2^{18}\}$ is a reduced residue system modulo 19.

4. If $m > 2$, show that $\phi(m)$ is even.

5. If $m > 1$, prove that the sum of the $\phi(m)$ positive integers which are less than m and relatively prime to m is $m\phi(m)/2$. [*Hint:* If $(a, m) = 1$, then also $(m - a, m) = 1$.]

6. If $m > 2$, prove that the sum of the integers in any reduced residue system modulo m is divisible by m.

7. Prove that $\phi(m^2) = m\phi(m)$ for each positive integer m.

8. Use Theorem 2.30 to show that if m and n are positive integers with $(m, n) = d$, then

$$\phi(mn) = \frac{d\phi(m)\phi(n)}{\phi(d)}.$$

9. Use the following hints to give an alternative proof that if m and n are positive integers with $(m, n) = 1$, then $\phi(mn) = \phi(m)\phi(n)$:

    (i)   The positive integers which are not greater than mn are the integers $qn + r$, where $q = 0, 1, \ldots, m - 1$ and $r = 1, 2, \ldots, n$.

    (ii) $(qn + r, n) = 1$ if and only if $(r, n) = 1$; hence there are $\phi(n)$ choices of r such that $qn + r$ is relatively prime to n for every q.

    (iii) For each r, the set $\{qn + r; q = 0, 1, \ldots, m - 1\}$ contains $\phi(m)$ elements which are relatively prime to m (cf. Theorem 2.15).

2.3   THE ORDER OF AN INTEGER MODULO m

The following important theorem of Euler is a fairly easy consequence of previous results.

2.35   EULER'S THEOREM. *If $(a, m) = 1$, then $a^{\phi(m)} \equiv 1 \pmod{m}$.*

PROOF: Let $\{r_1, r_2, \ldots, r_{\phi(m)}\}$ be a reduced residue system modulo m. Since $(a, m) = 1$, Theorem 2.20 implies that $\{ar_1, ar_2, \ldots, ar_{\phi(m)}\}$ also is a reduced residue system modulo m. By Lemma 2.21, we therefore have that

$$\prod_{i=1}^{\phi(m)} (ar_i) \equiv \prod_{i=1}^{\phi(m)} r_i \pmod{m},$$

or

$$a^{\phi(m)} \prod_{i=1}^{\phi(m)} r_i \equiv \prod_{i=1}^{\phi(m)} r_i \ (\mathrm{mod} \ m).$$

However, since the elements of a reduced residue system modulo m are relatively prime to m, we can cancel the indicated products from both sides of this congruence and obtain

$$a^{\phi(m)} \equiv 1 \ (\mathrm{mod} \ m).$$

The proof is therefore completed.

The important special case of this result in which m is a prime is due to Fermat. If p is a prime, then $(a, p) = 1$ if and only if $p \nmid a$. Moreover, $\phi(p) = p - 1$, so we obtain at once the following result.

2.36 FERMAT'S THEOREM. *If p is a prime and $p \nmid a$, then $a^{p-1} \equiv 1$ (mod p).*

The following result, which is essentially a reformulation of Fermat's Theorem is sometimes useful.

2.37 *If p is a prime, then $a^p \equiv a$ (mod p) for every integer a.*

Clearly, if $a^{p-1} \equiv 1$ (mod p), then $a^p \equiv a$ (mod p), so if $p \nmid a$, the desired result is true by Fermat's Theorem. If $p \mid a$, then $a \equiv 0$ (mod p) and also $a^p \equiv 0$ (mod p), so in this case it is trivial that $a^p \equiv a$ (mod p). Hence $a^p \equiv a$ (mod p) for every integer a.

We next define an important new concept. If a is relatively prime to m, Euler's Theorem asserts that there always exists a positive integer s (namely, $\phi(m)$) such that $a^s \equiv 1$ (mod m).

2.38 DEFINITION. If $(a, m) = 1$, the smallest positive integer r such that $a^r \equiv 1$ (mod m) is called the *order* of a modulo m.*

By Euler's Theorem, the order of a modulo m does not exceed $\phi(m)$. We may also observe that if $a \equiv b$ (mod m) and a has order r modulo m, then clearly b also has order r modulo m. That is, all the integers in a given residue class modulo m (consisting of integers relatively prime to m) have the same order modulo m.

Let us emphasize that if $a^s \equiv 1$ (mod m) for some positive integer s, then we must have $(a, m) = 1$. Thus the concept of order of a modulo m is meaningful if and only if $(a, m) = 1$. In the future, when we refer to the order of a modulo m, it is to be assumed that $(a, m) = 1$, even if it is not explicitly stated.

---

*In the literature, what we have called "the order of a modulo m" is often called "the exponent of a modulo m" or "the exponent to which a belongs modulo m."

We proceed to establish several fundamental results related to this concept of order. Some additional results will also be obtained in the following chapter.

2.39   THEOREM. *If a has order r modulo m and k is a positive integer, then $a^k \equiv 1 \pmod{m}$ if and only if $r \mid k$.*

PROOF: Suppose, first, that $k = rs$. Since $a^r \equiv 1 \pmod{m}$, it follows by 2.8 that $(a^r)^s \equiv 1^s \pmod{m}$, or that $a^k \equiv 1 \pmod{m}$.

Next, let k be a positive integer such that $a^k \equiv 1 \pmod{m}$. Clearly, $k \geq r$, since a has order r modulo m. By the division algorithm, there exists a positive integer q and a nonnegative integer t such that $k = qr + t$, where $0 \leq t < r$. Thus $a^k = a^{qr} \cdot a^t$ and since $a^k \equiv 1 \pmod{m}$ by hypothesis and $a^{qr} \equiv 1 \pmod{m}$ by the part of the theorem already proved, it follows that $a^t \equiv 1 \pmod{m}$. Now by the definition of the order r of a modulo m, t cannot be a positive integer less than r. Hence we must have $t = 0$ and we conclude that $k = qr$, completing the proof.

In view of Euler's Theorem, we have the following immediate corollary of the theorem just established.

2.40   COROLLARY. *For each integer a such that $(a, m) = 1$, the order of a modulo m is a divisor of $\phi(m)$.*

Next, let us prove the following result.

2.41   THEOREM. *If a has order r modulo m, and i and j are nonnegative integers, then $a^i \equiv a^j \pmod{m}$ if and only if $i \equiv j \pmod{r}$. In particular, the elements of the set $\{a, a^2, \ldots, a^r\}$ are incongruent modulo m.*

PROOF: If $i \neq j$, we may just as well assume that the notation is so chosen that $i > j$. Since $(a, m) = 1$, it follows that $a^i \equiv a^j \pmod{m}$ if and only if $a^{i-j} \equiv 1 \pmod{m}$. By Theorem 2.39, this last congruence holds if and only if $r \mid (i - j)$, that is, if and only if $i \equiv j \pmod{r}$. The last statement of the theorem is now an immediate consequence of the fact that the elements of the set $\{1, 2, \ldots, r\}$ are incongruent modulo r.

Since, by 2.19, any set of $\phi(m)$ integers which are relatively prime to m and incongruent modulo m is a reduced residue system modulo m, we have the following corollary of the preceding theorem.

2.42   COROLLARY. *If a has order $\phi(m)$ modulo m, then $\{a, a^2, \ldots, a^{\phi(m)}\}$ is a reduced residue system modulo m.*

The statement of this corollary is not meant to imply that if m is a given positive integer there necessarily exists an integer of order $\phi(m)$ modulo m. We shall see later that such an integer does exist for some choices of m but not for others.

2.43 THEOREM. *If a has order r modulo m and k is a positive integer, then a^k has order $r/(k, r)$ modulo m.*

PROOF: If s is a positive integer, then Theorem 2.39 shows that

$$(a^k)^s \equiv a^{ks} \equiv 1 \pmod{m}$$

if and only if $r \mid ks$. Let us set $d = (k, r)$, $r = r_1 d$ and $k = k_1 d$. Then $r \mid ks$ if and only if $r_1 \mid k_1 s$. However, $(r_1, k_1) = 1$, so $r_1 \mid k_1 s$ if and only if $r_1 \mid s$. We have therefore shown that $(a^k)^s \equiv 1 \pmod{m}$ if and only if $r_1 \mid s$. Clearly, the smallest such positive integer s is r_1, and a^k has order r_1 modulo m. Since $r_1 = r/(k, r)$, the proof is completed.

2.44 COROLLARY. *If a has order r modulo m and k is a positive integer, then a^k also has order r modulo m if and only if $(k, r) = 1$.*

2.45 COROLLARY. *If a has order r modulo m, there are exactly $\phi(r)$ numbers of the set $\{a, a^2, \ldots, a^r\}$ which have order r modulo m.*

Let us now give numerical illustrations of some of the results of this section.

First, let $m = 14$. Then $\phi(14) = 6$, so that every integer which is relatively prime to 14 has order modulo 14 a divisor of 6. Let us determine the orders of the elements of the reduced residue system $\{1, 3, 5, -5, -3, -1\}$ modulo 14. Clearly, 1 has order 1 modulo 14. Since $3^2 \equiv 9 \pmod{14}$ and $3^3 \equiv 27 \equiv -1 \pmod{14}$, we see that 3 cannot have order 1, 2, or 3; hence it must have order 6. The following table gives the orders modulo 14 of all the elements of the reduced residue system exhibited above.

Integer	1	3	5	-5	-3	-1
Order	1	6	6	3	3	2

We observe that there exists an integer which has order modulo 14 any given divisor of $\phi(14)$. Moreover, the reader may illustrate the truth of Corollary 2.42 in this case by verifying that each of the sets $\{3, 3^2, 3^3, 3^4, 3^5, 3^6\}$ and $\{5, 5^2, 5^3, 5^4, 5^5, 5^6\}$ is a reduced residue system modulo 14.

As a second example, let $m = 15$. Then $\phi(15) = 8$. The orders modulo 15 of the elements of the reduced residue system $\{1, 2, 4, 7, -7, -4, -2, -1\}$ are given in the following table.

Integer	1	2	4	7	-7	-4	-2	-1
Order	1	4	2	4	4	2	4	2

This shows that there is no integer of order $\phi(15)$ modulo 15.

We have observed that there exists an integer which has order $\phi(14)$ modulo 14, but that there does not exist an integer which has order $\phi(15)$ modulo 15. However, we shall postpone until the next chapter a determination of those integers m for which there does exist an integer of order $\phi(m)$ modulo m.

Exercises

1. Find the order of 5 modulo 12; of 3 modulo 20; of 2 modulo 17; of 2^{12} modulo 17; of 13 modulo 7.

2. Determine whether there exists an integer which has order $\phi(m)$ modulo m for each of the following choices of m: 5, 11, 12, 13, 22.

3. If $ab \equiv 1 \pmod{m}$, prove that a and b have the same order modulo m.

4. Prove that if a has order r modulo m and order s modulo n and if $(r, s) = 1$, then a has order rs modulo $[m, n]$.

5. Prove that if a has order r modulo m and b has order s modulo m and if $(r, s) = 1$, then ab has order rs modulo m. [*Hint:* If $(ab)^t \equiv 1 \pmod{m}$, then $(ab)^{rt} \equiv 1 \pmod{m}$, etc.]

6. Prove that for each positive integer $n \geq 2$, the order of 5 modulo 2^n is 2^{n-2}. [*Hint:* Prove by induction that there exists an odd integer k_n such that $5^{2^{n-2}} = 1 + k_n 2^n$.]

7. Suppose that $(a, m) = 1$ and $(b, m) = 1$, and consider the smallest positive integer t such that $a^t \equiv b^t \pmod{m}$. Prove that if x is a positive integer such that $a^x \equiv b^x \pmod{m}$, then $t \mid x$.

8. Suppose that there exists an integer a which has order $\phi(m)$ modulo m and that $d \mid \phi(m)$. Use 2.32, 2.43, and 2.42 to prove that in each reduced residue system modulo m there exist precisely $\phi(d)$ integers which have order d modulo m.

2.4   PERIODIC DECIMALS

We now pause briefly in our development of the fundamental properties of congruence to give a simple application of a few of the results already established. It will be necessary to make use of some properties of infinite decimals which we shall here state without proof.

Let k be a nonnegative integer and suppose that $n_0, n_1, \ldots, n_k$ and m_i $(i = 1, 2, 3, \ldots)$ are integers from the set $\{0, 1, \ldots, 9\}$. The infinite series

2.46
$$n_k 10^k + \cdots + n_0 + \sum_{i=1}^{\infty} \frac{m_i}{10^i}$$

may be written in the following familiar decimal notation:

2.47 $\qquad\qquad\qquad n_k \cdots n_0 . m_1 m_2 m_3 \cdots .$

Such a series always converges to a nonnegative real number α, and it is customary to write

2.48 $\qquad\qquad\qquad \alpha = n_k \cdots n_0 . m_1 m_2 m_3 \cdots .$

Moreover, the right side of this equation may be called a *decimal representation* of the real number α, and α may be called the *value* of this decimal.

If there exists a nonnegative integer l such that in 2.47 all $m_i = 0$ for $i > l$, we may simply omit all these zeros and, assuming that l is chosen as small as possible, speak of a finite decimal of *length* l. A decimal which is not finite is naturally an *infinite* decimal. We may point out that, according to the present definition, a positive integer is represented by a finite decimal of length zero.

A real number which can be represented by a finite decimal also has a representation as an infinite decimal. For example,

$$.24 = .23999 \cdots ,$$

it being understood that 9 is repeated indefinitely. However, if we agree (as we do henceforth) never to admit an infinite decimal with all 9's from some point on, it can be shown that every positive real number has exactly one decimal representation. Accordingly, we may speak of *the* decimal representation of a given positive real number.

If the real number α has the decimal representation 2.48, then the integral part $[\alpha]$ of α (as defined in 1.48) is the integer $n_k \cdots n_0$, and the decimal $.m_1 m_2 m_3 \cdots$ whose value is $\alpha - [\alpha]$ may be called the *decimal part* of α.

As a matter of notation, let us indicate the indefinite repetition of a finite sequence of digits by placing a bar over these digits. Thus, for example, $152.4\overline{81}$ indicates the infinite decimal $152.4818181 \cdots$ in which 81 is repeated indefinitely. We may call this decimal a *periodic* decimal (or a *repeating* decimal) with 4 as the *nonperiodic part* and 81 as the *period*. Also, it will be convenient to say that the nonperiodic part has *length* one (since it contains one digit) and that the period has *length* two. It will be observed that these concepts involve only the decimal part of the number and do not depend upon the integral part (152 in this example).

Decimals are of various kinds as illustrated in the following examples:

(i) .24,   (ii) .$\overline{34}$,   (iii) .21$\overline{296}$,   (iv) .01001000100001 $\cdots$.

In Example (i) we have a finite decimal of length two. Since there is no nonperiodic part in Example (ii) (that is, the nonperiodic part has length zero), it is sometimes said to be a *purely* periodic decimal in which the period has length two. The decimal in Example (iii) has a nonperiodic part of length two and a period of length three. In Example (iv), we mean to imply that one more zero is to be inserted each time, and it is therefore a nonperiodic decimal.

Let us make one further agreement as follows. Although, for example, .2$\overline{34}$ = .2$\overline{3434}$ = .2$\overline{3434}$, we say that this decimal has period 34 (not 3434) and that 2 (not 234) is the nonperiodic part. In general, if we say that a decimal has a nonperiodic part of length s and a period of length t, it is to be understood that both s and t are chosen as small as possible. We may emphasize that these concepts refer only to the decimal part of a number and have nothing to do with the integral part of the number.

As a matter of language, we shall not consider a finite decimal to be a periodic decimal, so that when we speak of a periodic decimal we always mean to imply that it is an infinite decimal.

In the next two theorems, of which the second is the principal theorem of this section, we shall show that the positive real numbers which have finite or periodic decimal representations are precisely the positive rational numbers. Moreover, we shall describe the form of the decimal representation of a given positive rational number. Of course, we shall assume that rational numbers are in lowest terms, that is, in the form a/b, where a and b are positive integers with $(a, b) = 1$.

The finite decimal case is easily disposed of in the following theorem.

2.49   THEOREM. (i) *If α is a positive real number with a finite decimal representation, then $\alpha = a/b$, where a and b are positive integers such that $(a, b) = 1$ and b has no prime factor except possibly 2 and 5.*

(ii)   *If a and b are positive integers such that $(a, b) = 1$ and if $b = 2^u \cdot 5^v$, where u and v are nonnegative integers, then a/b has a finite decimal representaiion of length max $\{u, v\}$.*

PROOF: For any positive real number α and any positive integer s, the decimal representation of $10^s\alpha$ can be obtained from the decimal representation of α by moving the decimal point s places to the right. Hence α has a finite decimal representation of length s if and only if $10^s\alpha$ is an integer and $10^k\alpha$ is not an integer for each nonnegative integer $k < s$.

Now suppose that $10^s\alpha = n$ for some positive integer n. Then $\alpha = n/10^s$ and since 10 has only the prime factors 2 and 5, if the rational number α is put in lowest terms by canceling $(n, 10^s)$ from the numerator and denominator, we obtain $\alpha = a/b$, where $(a, b) = 1$ and b has no prime factor except possibly 2 and 5.

Next, let a and b be positive integers such that $(a, b) = 1$ and $b = 2^u \cdot 5^v$ for nonnegative integers u and v. If $s = \max \{u, v\}$, then s is the smallest nonnegative integer such that $10^s(a/b) = (2^s \cdot 5^s \cdot a)/b$ is an integer. Accordingly, a/b has a finite decimal representation of length s. This completes the proof of the theorem.

In the next theorem we shall finally make essential use of some of the previous concepts of this chapter.

2.50   THEOREM. (i) *If α is a positive real number with a periodic decimal representation, then $\alpha = a/b$, where a and b are positive integers such that $(a, b) = 1$ and b has at least one prime factor other than 2 and 5.*

(ii)   *Let a and b be positive integers such that $(a, b) = 1$ and suppose that b has at least one prime factor other than 2 and 5. Thus we may write $b = 2^u \cdot 5^v c$, where u and v are nonnegative integers, $c > 1$, and $(c, 10) = 1$. Then a/b has a periodic decimal representation with nonperiodic part of length $\max \{u, v\}$ and period of length equal to the order of 10 modulo c.*

PROOF: First, let us observe for future reference that if β and γ are positive real numbers, then $\beta - \gamma$ is an integer if and only if β and γ have the same decimal parts.

We now proceed to prove part (i) of the theorem. Suppose that α is a periodic decimal

2.51 $n_k \cdots n_0 . m_1 m_2 \cdots \overline{m_s m_{s+1} \cdots m_{s+t}}$

with nonperiodic part of length s and period of length t. Then $10^s \alpha$ and $10^{s+t} \alpha$ have the same decimal parts and, by the observation made above, there exists an integer n (which we need not bother to compute) such that

$$10^{s+t} \alpha - 10^s \alpha = n.$$

It follows that

$$\alpha = \frac{n}{10^s(10^t - 1)},$$

and α is a rational number. Moreover, when expressed in lowest terms a/b, we know that b must contain some prime factor other than 2 and 5 since, otherwise, Theorem 2.49 would show that a/b has a *finite* decimal representation. This completes the proof of the first part of the theorem.

Now let a and b be as in the statement of part (ii) of the theorem. For arbitrary positive integers a_1 and a_2, the observation made at the beginning of the proof shows that the decimal representations of a_1/b and a_2/b have the same decimal parts if and only if $(a_1 - a_2)/b$ is an integer, that is, if and only if $a_1 \equiv a_2 \pmod{b}$. Since there are at most b incongruent integers modulo b, there must be at least two distinct integers in the set $\{a, 10a, 10^2a, \ldots, 10^ba\}$ which are congruent modulo b. Thus there exists a nonnegative integer s, which we shall assume chosen as small as possible, such that $10^s a$ is congruent modulo b to some other element of this set. Let t then be the smallest positive integer such that

$$2.52 \qquad\qquad 10^s a \equiv 10^{s+t}a \pmod{b}.$$

It follows that $10^s a$ and $10^{s+t}a$ have the same decimal parts and this implies (why?) that a/b has a periodic decimal representation of the form 2.51 with s the length of the nonperiodic part and t the length of the period. To complete the proof, we need only determine the smallest values of s and t such that the congruence 2.52 is satisfied. Since $(a, b) = 1$, we may cancel a from both sides of this congruence. Hence congruence 2.52 holds if and only if

$$10^s(10^t - 1) \equiv 0 \pmod{b}.$$

Using the assumed fact that $b = 2^u \cdot 5^v \cdot c$, where $c > 1$ and $(c, 10) = 1$, the preceding congruence holds if and only if $10^s \equiv 0 \pmod{2^u \cdot 5^v}$ and $10^t - 1 \equiv 0 \pmod{c}$. Hence the smallest value of s is max $\{u, v\}$ and the smallest positive value of t is the order of 10 modulo c. This completes the proof of the theorem.

It is an interesting fact that the conclusions in the second part of this theorem do not depend upon the numerator a of the rational number a/b in lowest terms.

As an illustration of the second part of the theorem, let us consider the decimal representation of a rational number of the form $a/74$, where $(a, 74) = 1$. Since $74 = 2 \cdot 37$ with $(37, 10) = 1$, in the notation of the theorem we have $u = 1$, $v = 0$, and $c = 37$. Moreover, a simple calculation will show that $10^2 \not\equiv 1 \pmod{37}$, but that $10^3 \equiv 1 \pmod{37}$, and hence that the order of 10 modulo 37 is three. Therefore, the decimal representation of $a/37$ must have a nonperiodic part of length $1 = \max\{1, 0\}$ and a period of length three. As a verification of these

$$
\begin{array}{r}
.1486 \\
74 \overline{\smash{)}\ 11.0000} \\
\underline{74} \\
360 \\
\underline{296} \\
640 \\
\underline{592} \\
480 \\
\underline{444} \\
36
\end{array}
$$

facts for a particular choice of a, let us compute the decimal representation of 11/74 by the familiar long division process of arithmetic. Since we obtain the same remainder, namely, 36, in the division of $10 \cdot 11$ by 74 as in the division of $10^4 \cdot 11$ by 74, the calculations repeat giving us $11/74 = .1\overline{486}$. In the notation of the above proof, we have $10 \cdot 11 \equiv 10^4 \cdot 11$ (mod 74), so that $s = 1$ and $t = 3$.

Exercises

1. Apply Theorem 2.50 to find the nature of the decimal representation of 5/13, and check by actually finding the representation.

2. Do the same for 1/770.

3. Apply Theorem 2.50 to find the nature of the decimal representation of each of the following: 1/37, 1/32, 1/80, 1/17, 1/27, 1/505.

4. What is the length of the nonperiodic part in the decimal representation of 1/1000!?

5. Find all positive integers b such that the decimal representation of $1/b$ is purely periodic with period of length 2.

6. Do the same for period of length 3.

2.5 LINEAR CONGRUENCES

We begin this section with a few remarks about polynomial congruences in general. Let

$$
2.53 \qquad\qquad f(x) = \sum_{i=0}^{n} a_i x^i
$$

be a polynomial with integral coefficients and, as usual, let m be a positive integer greater than 1. If c is an integer such that $f(c) \equiv 0$ (mod m), we may say that c *satisfies* the congruence

$$
2.54 \qquad\qquad f(x) \equiv 0 \ (\text{mod } m).
$$

By Theorem 2.9, if c satisfies this congruence and $c \equiv d$ (mod m), then d also satisfies the congruence. That is, if one element of a certain residue class modulo m satisfies the congruence, then all elements of that residue class satisfy the congruence. It is convenient to consider that all the elements of such a residue class constitute one *solution* of the congruence. Thus, if c satisfies the congruence 2.54, we shall say that $x \equiv c \pmod{m}$ is a solution of the congruence. Solutions $x \equiv c_1 \pmod{m}$ and $x \equiv c_2 \pmod{m}$ of the congruence 2.54 are therefore to be considered as different solutions if and only if $c_1 \not\equiv c_2 \pmod{m}$. Accordingly, the number of solutions of a congruence 2.54 is the number of incongruent integers which satisfy the congruence, that is, the number of integers in a complete residue system modulo m which satisfy the congruence. In particular, the number of solutions of a polynomial congruence modulo m is the number of integers in the set $\{0, 1, \ldots, m - 1\}$ which satisfy the congruence. If m is small, it may thus be quite easy to determine all solutions by a simple trial and error method.

As an example, let $f(x) = 2x^2 + 3x + 1$, and consider the congruence $f(x) \equiv 0 \pmod{6}$. By simply trying in turn the numbers 0, 1, 2, 3, 4, 5, we find that 1 and 5 satisfy this congruence and the other numbers do not. Hence the solutions of this congruence are $x \equiv 1 \pmod{6}$ and $x \equiv 5 \pmod{6}$. This statement is, of course, equivalent to the statement that the integers which satisfy the congruence are precisely those integers of the form $1 + 6t$ or $5 + 6t$ for an arbitrary integer t.

If $f(x)$ is given as in 2.53 and if $a_n \not\equiv 0 \pmod{m}$, we say that the congruence $f(x) \equiv 0 \pmod{m}$ is of *degree* n modulo m. In the example of the preceding paragraph we had a congruence of degree two since $2 \not\equiv 0 \pmod{6}$. The concept of the degree of a polynomial modulo m or of a polynomial congruence modulo m will be presented somewhat more fully in the next chapter.

A congruence of degree one is often called a *linear* congruence. Any linear congruence may clearly be written in the form $ax \equiv b \pmod{m}$, with $a \not\equiv 0 \pmod{m}$. We shall now prove an important result about the solutions of a linear congruence and postpone until later the study of congruences of higher degree.

2.55   THEOREM. *Suppose that $a \not\equiv 0 \pmod{m}$ and let $d = (a, m)$. Then the congruence*

2.56 $ax \equiv b \pmod{m}$

has a solution if and only if $d \mid b$. If $d \mid b$ and x_0 is any integer which satisfies the congruence, then the congruence has exactly d solutions as follows:

$$x \equiv x_0 + t(m/d) \pmod{m}, \qquad (t = 0, 1, \ldots, d - 1).$$

PROOF: By a change in the point of view, we shall find that this theorem follows quite easily from Theorem 1.20.

An integer x satisfies congruence 2.56 if and only if there is an integer z such that $ax - b = mz$ or, equally well, if and only if there is an integer $y(= -z)$ such that

$$ax + my = b.$$

Hence Theorem 1.20 (with n and b respectively replaced by b and m) shows that our congruence has a solution if and only if $d|b$. Assume, now, that $d|b$ and that x_0 satisfies our congruence. Again applying Theorem 1.20, we find that the integers which satisfy the congruence are precisely the integers of the set

$$S = \{x_0 + (m/d)t; t \in I\}.$$

To complete the proof of the theorem, we need to investigate just what different residue classes modulo m are included in the set S. If t_1 and t_2 are integers, then

$$x_0 + (m/d)t_1 \equiv x_0 + (m/d)t_2 \pmod{m}$$

if and only if

$$(m/d)t_1 \equiv (m/d)t_2 \pmod{m}$$

or (by 2.10) if and only if

$$t_1 \equiv t_2 \pmod{d}.$$

Hence by letting t vary over the complete residue system $\{0, 1, \ldots, d - 1\}$ modulo d, we find that the integers of the set

$$T = \{x_0, x_0 + (m/d), x_0 + 2(m/d), \ldots, x_0 + (d - 1)(m/d)\}$$

are incongruent modulo m and that every integer of the set S is congruent modulo m to one of the integers of the set T. Accordingly, we have exactly d solutions of the congruence 2.56 as specified in the statement of the theorem.

The following special case is of such importance that we state it explicitly.

2.57 COROLLARY. *If $(a, m) = 1$, the congruence $ax \equiv b \pmod{m}$ always has a unique solution.*

Suppose, now, that R is a reduced residue system modulo m. If $r \in R$ and $(t, m) = 1$, the congruence $rx \equiv t \pmod{m}$ has a unique solution, since $(r, m) = 1$. Moreover, if x_0 satisfies this congruence, we must have $(x_0, m) = 1$ since $(t, m) = 1$. Hence x_0 is congruent modulo

m to exactly one element of R, and we have established the following result.

2.58 COROLLARY. *Let R be a reduced residue system modulo m, and suppose that $(t, m) = 1$. If $r \in R$, there exists exactly one element s of R such that $rs \equiv t \pmod{m}$.*

It may be of interest to point out that Euler's Theorem (2.35) makes it possible to exhibit the unique solution of the congruence $ax \equiv b \pmod{m}$ if $(a, m) = 1$. For, since in this case $a^{\phi(m)} \equiv 1 \pmod{m}$, we see that

$$a(ba^{\phi(m)-1}) \equiv b \pmod{m},$$

and we have established the following result.

2.59 COROLLARY. *If $(a, m) = 1$, the unique solution of the congruence $ax \equiv b \pmod{m}$ is $x \equiv ba^{\phi(m)-1} \pmod{m}$.*

It will be observed in the first example below that the theoretical solution given in this corollary may be of no value when a numerical calculation is involved.

Example 1. Solve the congruence $13x \equiv 3 \pmod{47}$.

Solution: Since $(13, 47) = 1$, this congruence has a unique solution. By Corollary 2.59, the solution is easy to exhibit as follows: $x \equiv 3 \cdot 13^{45} \pmod{47}$. However, it would take an unreasonable amount of work to find the smallest positive residue of $3 \cdot 13^{45}$ modulo 47 and thus to obtain the solution in a simple form.

Another approach would be to test in turn the integers $0, 1, 2, \ldots, 46$ until we find the unique one which satisfies the given congruence. For a small modulus this procedure might be very reasonable but probably not for a modulus as large as 47.

Let us proceed to use a method which is essentially suggested by the proof of Theorem 1.20 and which will be seen to involve only a modest amount of calculation. We begin by expressing 1 as a linear combination of the relatively prime integers 13 and 47 by use of the Euclidean algorithm as in Section 1.3. We omit the details here, but it may be found in this way that

$$1 = 5 \cdot 47 - 18 \cdot 13.$$

Accordingly, we have that

$$13(-18) \equiv 1 \pmod{47}.$$

Multiplying both sides of this congruence by 3 gives us the congruence

$$13(-54) \equiv 3 \pmod{47}$$

and hence the given congruence $13x \equiv 3 \pmod{47}$ has the solution $x \equiv -54 \pmod{47}$. However, $-54 \equiv -7 \equiv 40 \pmod{47}$, so the solution is also given by $x \equiv -7 \pmod{47}$ or by $x \equiv 40 \pmod{47}$. (What is the least positive residue of $3 \cdot 13^{45}$ modulo 47?)

Example 2. Solve the congruence $36x \equiv 27 \pmod{45}$.

Solution: Since $(36, 45) = 9$ and $9|27$, Theorem 2.55 shows that this congruence has nine solutions. Moreover, we can write down all of them as soon as we know some one integer which satisfies the congruence. In this case we proceed as follows.

The congruence

2.60 $$4x \equiv 3 \pmod{5}$$

is satisfied by exactly the same integers as the congruence

2.61 $$36x \equiv 27 \pmod{45}.$$

It is easy to verify by inspection that the integer 2 satisfies the congruence 2.60. Hence, Theorem 2.55 gives us the nine solutions of the congruence 2.61 as follows:

$$x \equiv 2 + 5t \pmod{45}, \qquad\qquad (t = 0, 1, 2, \ldots, 8.)$$

It may be worth emphasizing that although the congruences 2.60 and 2.61 are satisfied by the same integers, the congruence 2.60 has the unique solution $x \equiv 2 \pmod{5}$. Of course, the explanation of this phenomenon is that the concept of *solution* depends upon the modulus. The numbers $2 + 5t$, where $t = 0, 1, 2, \ldots, 8$, are incongruent modulo 45, but all are congruent to 2 modulo 5.

Remark. Let $R = \{r_1, r_2, \ldots, r_{\phi(m)}\}$ be a reduced residue system modulo m. If $r_i, r_j \in R$, then $r_i r_j$ is relatively prime to m, and hence there exists a unique element r_k of R such that $r_i r_j \equiv r_k \pmod{m}$. If we set $r_i \circ r_j = r_k$, then $\circ$ is an operation defined on the set R. With respect to this operation, we assert that R is a *group*. The identity is clearly the element, say r_1, of R such that $r_1 \equiv 1 \pmod{m}$. If $r_i \in R$, Corollary 2.58 shows that there is an element r_l of R such that $r_i \circ r_l = r_1$, that is, r_i has an inverse r_l in R. Since the operation $\circ$ is clearly associative (why?), we have verified that R is indeed a group. Now this group has *order* $\phi(m)$, that is, has $\phi(m)$ elements, and each integer a which is relatively prime to m is congruent modulo m to an element of the set R. The reader with some knowledge of finite groups will therefore recognize that Euler's Theorem is merely a statement, for this particular group, of a well-known theorem about finite groups.

Another description of the group just exhibited is as follows. Let R be the set given above and let $G = \{E_{r_1}, E_{r_2}, \ldots, E_{r_{\phi(m)}}\}$, where E_r is the residue class to which r belongs modulo m. If we define $E_{r_i} \cdot E_{r_j} = E_{r_i r_j}$, (as in defining the ring of integers modulo m), then we have an operation on G with respect to which G is a group. In other words, under the usual definition of multiplication of residue classes, the set of all residue classes modulo m which consist of integers that are relatively prime to m is a group of order $\phi(m)$. The mapping $r \to E_r, r \in R$, is an isomorphism of the group R, as defined in the preceding paragraph, onto the group G.

Exercises

1. Find all solutions of each of the following congruences:

(i) $x^2 + x + 1 \equiv 0 \pmod{11}$,   (ii) $3x^2 + 2x + 2 \equiv 0 \pmod 6$,

(iii) $x^5 - x \equiv 0 \pmod 5$,   (iv) $x^3 + x^2 - 2x \equiv 0 \pmod 6$,

(v) $x^2 - 6x - 6 \equiv 0 \pmod{11}$,   (vi) $x^3 \equiv x^2 \pmod{12}$.

2. Find all solutions of each of the following linear congruences:

(i) $11x \equiv 2 \pmod{40}$,   (ii) $12x \equiv 25 \pmod{97}$,

(iii) $17x \equiv 11 \pmod{300}$,   (iv) $15x \equiv 10 \pmod{85}$,

(v) $24x \equiv 18 \pmod{606}$,   (vi) $13x \equiv 4 \pmod{53}$,

(vii) $4x \equiv 7 \pmod{30}$,   (viii) $21x \equiv 12 \pmod{330}$.

3. Prove that every odd integer satisfies the congruence $x^{17} - x \equiv 0 \pmod{15 \cdot 17 \cdot 32}$.

4. Find all solutions of the congruence $x^{22} + 2x^{11} + 9 \equiv 0 \pmod{11}$.

5. If $m = 7 \cdot 13 \cdot 19$, verify that the congruence $x^{m-1} \equiv 1 \pmod m$ is satisfied by every integer which is relatively prime to m. Show that the order of every such integer modulo m is less than $m - 1$.

2.6　WILSON'S THEOREM AND EULER'S CRITERION

Before stating the next theorem, let us establish the following simple preliminary result.

2.62 LEMMA. *Let p be an odd prime and a an integer such that $(a, p) = 1$. If the congruence $x^2 \equiv a \pmod p$ has a solution $x \equiv x_0 \pmod p$, then $(x_0, p) = 1$ and the congruence has exactly two solutions $x \equiv x_0 \pmod p$ and $x \equiv -x_0 \pmod p$.*

PROOF: Since $(a, p) = 1$, if $x_0^2 \equiv a \pmod p$, clearly we must have

$(x_0, p) = 1$. Moreover, $(-x_0)^2 \equiv a \pmod{p}$ and $x_0 \not\equiv -x_0 \pmod{p}$, since otherwise $2x_0$ would be divisible by the odd prime p, and this is impossible. Hence the solutions $x \equiv x_0 \pmod{p}$ and $x \equiv -x_0 \pmod{p}$ are distinct solutions. There remains only to prove that there are no other solutions.

Suppose that t is any integer such that $t^2 \equiv a \pmod{p}$. Since $x_0^2 \equiv a \pmod{p}$, it follows that $t^2 \equiv x_0^2 \pmod{p}$ or that $(t - x_0)(t + x_0) \equiv 0 \pmod{p}$. However, since p is a prime, this implies that $t - x_0 \equiv 0 \pmod{p}$ or that $t + x_0 \equiv 0 \pmod{p}$, that is, that $t \equiv x_0 \pmod{p}$ or $t \equiv -x_0 \pmod{p}$. Thus the two solutions we have found are the only solutions, and the proof is completed.

We may emphasize that this lemma gives no information about whether a congruence $x^2 \equiv a \pmod{p}$ does or does not have a solution. For example, it is easy to verify by direct calculation that the congruence $x^2 \equiv 3 \pmod{7}$ does not have a solution, whereas the congruence $x^2 \equiv 2 \pmod{7}$ does have a solution. The next theorem will presently lead us to an important criterion (2.73) as to whether a congruence $x^2 \equiv a \pmod{p}$ has a solution.

2.63   THEOREM. *Let p be an odd prime, let R be a reduced residue system modulo p, and suppose that $(a, p) = 1$.*

(i)   *If the congruence $x^2 \equiv a \pmod{p}$ has a solution, then*

2.64
$$\prod_{r \in R} r \equiv -a^{(p-1)/2} \pmod{p}.$$

(ii)   *If the congruence $x^2 \equiv a \pmod{p}$ does not have a solution, then*

2.65
$$\prod_{r \in R} r \equiv a^{(p-1)/2} \pmod{p}.$$

Proof of (i). Since we are assuming that the congruence $x^2 \equiv a \pmod{p}$ has a solution, the preceding lemma shows that there are two distinct elements of R, say r_1 and r_2, which satisfy this congruence. Moreover, $r_1 \equiv -r_2 \pmod{p}$, and it follows that $r_1 r_2 \equiv -r_2^2 \pmod{p}$, that is, that

2.66
$$r_1 r_2 \equiv -a \pmod{p}.$$

We proceed to pair off all other elements of R in such a way that the product of the elements in each pair is congruent to a modulo p. Accordingly, let r_3 be an element of R distinct from r_1 and r_2. By Corollary 2.58, there exists a unique element r_4 of R such that

2.67
$$r_3 r_4 \equiv a \pmod{p}.$$

Now we know that $r_3 \neq r_4$ since r_1 and r_2 are the only elements of R which satisfy the congruence $x^2 \equiv a \pmod{p}$. We leave it to the reader to verify that, in fact, $r_4 \neq r_i$ ($i = 1, 2, 3$). If R has more than four elements, let r_5 be an element of R such that $r_5 \neq r_i$ ($i = 1, 2, 3, 4$), and r_6 the unique element of R such that

$$2.68 \qquad\qquad\qquad r_5 r_6 \equiv a \pmod{p}.$$

Again, $r_6 \neq r_i$ ($i = 1, 2, 3, 4, 5$). By a continuation of this procedure, we obtain a system of $(p - 1)/2$ congruences (2.66, 2.67, 2.68, etc.)

$$r_1 r_2 \equiv -a \pmod{p},$$
$$r_3 r_4 \equiv a \pmod{p},$$
$$2.69 \qquad\qquad r_5 r_6 \equiv a \pmod{p},$$
$$\cdots\cdots\cdots\cdots\cdots$$
$$r_{p-2} r_{p-1} \equiv a \pmod{p},$$

such that $r_1, r_2, \ldots, r_{p-1}$ are the elements of R in some order. Multiplying together corresponding sides of all these congruences, we obtain the congruence 2.64, thus completing the proof of this part of the theorem.

Proof of (ii). In this case we do not have the exceptional first congruence of 2.69. Instead, we can *always* obtain pairs of distinct elements of R whose product is congruent to a modulo p. We leave the details of the proof as an exercise.

The congruence $x^2 \equiv 1 \pmod{p}$ certainly has a solution; hence the following result is an immediate consequence of the first part of the preceding theorem.

2.70   COROLLARY. *If R is a reduced residue system modulo the prime p, then*

$$\prod_{r \in R} r \equiv -1 \pmod{p}.$$

In Theorem 2.63, we restricted p to be an odd prime, but the conclusion of Corollary 2.70 certainly holds also for $p = 2$ since $\{1\}$ is a reduced residue system modulo 2 and $1 \equiv -1 \pmod{2}$.

In the literature, a special case of Corollary 2.70 goes by the name of Wilson's Theorem. This theorem is obtained by letting $R = \{1, 2, \ldots, p - 1\}$ in Corollary 2.70.

2.71   WILSON'S THEOREM. *If p is a prime, then*

$$(p - 1)! \equiv -1 \ (\text{mod } p).$$

Before passing to the final theorem of this section, let us make the following simple observation.

2.72   LEMMA. *If p is an odd prime and $(a, p) = 1$, then one and only one of the following two congruences holds:*

$$a^{(p-1)/2} \equiv 1 \ (\text{mod } p), \quad a^{(p-1)/2} \equiv -1 \ (\text{mod } p).$$

First, we observe that both of these congruences cannot hold since this would imply that $1 \equiv -1 \ (\text{mod } p)$, and this is impossible since p is an odd prime.

The fact that one of the congruences must hold is implied by Theorem 2.63 and Corollary 2.70, but it is also an easy consequence of Fermat's Theorem as follows. The congruence $a^{p-1} \equiv 1 \ (\text{mod } p)$ may be written in the form

$$(a^{(p-1)/2} - 1)(a^{(p-1)/2} + 1) \equiv 0 \ (\text{mod } p),$$

and one of the factors on the left must be divisible by the prime p.

The following famous result of Euler now is an immediate consequence of Theorem 2.63 and Corollary 2.70.

2.73   EULER'S CRITERION. *If p is an odd prime and $(a, p) = 1$, then the congruence $x^2 \equiv a \ (\text{mod } p)$ has a solution or does not have a solution according as $a^{(p-1)/2} \equiv 1 \ (\text{mod } p)$ or $a^{(p-1)/2} \equiv -1 \ (\text{mod } p)$.*

Exercises

1.   Complete the proof of Theorem 2.63 (ii).

2.   Prove the following converse of Wilson's Theorem. If $(m - 1)! \equiv -1$ $(\text{mod } m)$, then m is a prime.

3.   Determine whether each of the following congruences has a solution:

(i) $x^2 \equiv 7 \ (\text{mod } 17)$,   (ii) $x^2 \equiv 3 \ (\text{mod } 29)$,

(iii) $x^2 \equiv 2 \ (\text{mod } 129)$,   (iv) $x^2 \equiv 150 \ (\text{mod } 151)$.

4.   Prove: If p is an odd prime such that the congruence $x^2 \equiv -1 \ (\text{mod } p)$ has a solution, the solutions are $x \equiv \pm\left(1 \cdot 2 \cdot 3 \cdots \dfrac{p-1}{2}\right) \ (\text{mod } p)$.

5.   If $\{r_1, r_2, \ldots, r_{p-1}\}$ and $\{s_1, s_2, \ldots, s_{p-1}\}$ are reduced residue systems modulo the odd prime p, prove that $\{r_1 s_1, r_2 s_2, \ldots, r_{p-1} s_{p-1}\}$ cannot be a reduced residue system modulo p.

2.7   SIMULTANEOUS LINEAR CONGRUENCES

Let us briefly consider the problem of solving a set of simultaneous linear congruences with different moduli. The following example will illustrate a simple procedure which, at least in theory, can always be applied if two or more linear congruences are explicitly given.

Example. Solve the simultaneous linear congruences

2.74
$$8x \equiv 4 \pmod{14},$$
$$5x \equiv 3 \pmod{11}.$$

Solution: We seek to find all integers which satisfy *both* of these congruences. It is easy to verify, using the theory developed in Section 2.5, that the single congruence $8x \equiv 4 \pmod{14}$ has the two solutions $x \equiv 4 \pmod{14}$ and $x \equiv 11 \pmod{14}$. Moreover, the single congruence $5x \equiv 3 \pmod{11}$ has the unique solution $x \equiv 5 \pmod{11}$. We seek therefore those integers which satisfy both of the congruences

2.75
$$x \equiv 4 \pmod{14},$$
$$x \equiv 5 \pmod{11},$$

and those integers which satisfy both of the congruences

2.76
$$x \equiv 11 \pmod{14},$$
$$x \equiv 5 \pmod{11},$$

since these are precisely the integers which satisfy the two given congruences 2.74.

Let us consider in detail the two congruences 2.75. The integers which satisfy the first congruence are the integers $4 + 14t$, $t \in I$. Next, an integer $4 + 14t$ will satisfy the second congruence if and only if

$$4 + 14t \equiv 5 \pmod{11},$$

or

$$3t \equiv 1 \pmod{11}.$$

The solution of this last congruence is $t \equiv 4 \pmod{11}$; hence $4 + 14t$ satisfies the second congruence of 2.75 if and only if $t = 4 + 11s$, $s \in I$. We have thus shown that the integers which satisfy both congruences 2.75 are precisely those integers of the form $4 + 14t$, where $t = 4 + 11s$, $s \in I$; that is, of the form $4 + 14(4 + 11s)$ or $60 + 154s$, $s \in I$. However, these are precisely the integers which are in the residue class modulo 154 which contains 60. Hence we may say that the simultaneous congruences 2.75 have the unique solution $x \equiv 60 \pmod{154}$.

In like manner, it can be shown that the simultaneous congruences 2.76 have the unique solution $x \equiv 137 \pmod{154}$. Hence the given congruences 2.74 have the two solutions $x \equiv 60 \pmod{154}$ and $x \equiv 137 \pmod{154}$.

Let us now briefly consider an arbitrary system of $k \geq 2$ simultaneous linear congruences

$$2.77 \qquad\qquad a_i x \equiv b_i \pmod{m_i}, \qquad (i = 1, 2, \ldots, k).$$

Certainly, this system has no solution unless each individual congruence has a solution. As in the example above, if each individual congruence has at least one solution, we can obtain all solutions of the system by solving simultaneously one or more systems of congruences of the following simple type:

$$2.78 \qquad\qquad x \equiv c_i \pmod{m_i}, \qquad (i = 1, 2, \ldots, k).$$

The case of most importance is that in which the moduli m_i are relatively prime in pairs, and in this case it can be proved that the integers which satisfy all of these congruences are precisely the integers in some one residue class modulo $m_1 m_2 \cdots m_k$. We state this fact as the following theorem.

2.79 CHINESE REMAINDER THEOREM. *Let m_i $(i = 1, 2, \ldots, k)$ be positive integers greater than 1 which are relatively prime in pairs, and let us set $m = m_1 m_2 \cdots m_k$. If c_i $(i = 1, 2, \ldots, k)$ are arbitrary integers, the simultaneous congruences 2.78 have a unique solution modulo m.*

PROOF: For each $i = 1, 2, \ldots, k$, let M_i be the product of those m_j with $j \neq i$. Then since the m_i are relatively prime in pairs, we have $(M_i, m_i) = 1$. Let T_i be an integer, whose existence is asserted by Corollary 2.57, such that $M_i T_i \equiv 1 \pmod{m_i}$. Since $M_j \equiv 0 \pmod{m_i}$ for $j \neq i$, it follows that for each $i = 1, 2, \ldots, k$,

$$c_1 M_1 T_1 + c_2 M_2 T_2 + \cdots + c_k M_k T_k \equiv c_i M_i T_i \equiv c_i \pmod{m_i}.$$

Hence the integer $u = c_1 M_1 T_1 + c_2 M_2 T_2 + \cdots + c_k M_k T_k$ satisfies all the congruences 2.78. If $v \equiv u \pmod{m}$, where $m = m_1 m_2 \cdots m_k$, clearly $v \equiv u \pmod{m_i}$ for $i = 1, 2, \ldots, k$, and v also satisfies the congruences 2.78. This shows that every integer in the residue class modulo m which contains u satisfies the congruences 2.78. We therefore say that $x \equiv u \pmod{m}$ is a solution of these congruences, and there remains only to prove that this is the only solution. Suppose that w is any integer which satisfies the congruences 2.78. Then $w \equiv u$ $\pmod{m_i}$ for $i = 1, 2, \ldots, k$, and (by 1.34 and 2.14) it follows that $w \equiv u \pmod{m}$, and w is in the same residue class modulo m as u. Hence the congruences 2.78 indeed have the unique solution $x \equiv u$ $\pmod{m}$, and the proof is completed.

As a simple illustration of the procedure used in the proof of this theorem, let us find the solution of the simultaneous congruences

$$x \equiv 3 \pmod{5}, \ x \equiv 5 \pmod{7}, \ x \equiv 2 \pmod{8}.$$

Here we have $c_1 = 3, c_2 = 5, c_3 = 2, m_1 = 5, m_2 = 7, m_3 = 8, M_1 = 56,$ $M_2 = 40,$ and $M_3 = 35.$ The congruence $56t \equiv 1 \pmod{5}$ is satisfied by $T_1 = 1$; the congruence $40t \equiv 1 \pmod{7}$ is satisfied by $T_2 = 3$; and the congruence $35t \equiv 1 \pmod{8}$ is satisfied by $T_3 = 3.$ Hence

$$u = 3 \cdot 56 \cdot 1 + 5 \cdot 40 \cdot 3 + 2 \cdot 35 \cdot 3 = 978$$

must satisfy our three given congruences. The unique solution is therefore $x \equiv 978 \pmod{280}$ or, in simpler form, $x \equiv 138 \pmod{280}$.

Exercises

1.   Find all solutions of each of the following sets of simultaneous linear congruences:

(i) $x \equiv 4 \pmod{13}, \ x \equiv 2 \pmod{17},$

(ii) $3x \equiv 7 \pmod{11}, \ 5x \equiv 2 \pmod{17},$

(iii) $23x \equiv 2 \pmod{26}, \ 26x \equiv 2 \pmod{23}.$

(iv) $x \equiv 1 \pmod{3}, \ x \equiv 2 \pmod{5}, \ x \equiv 3 \pmod{7},$

(v) $5x \equiv 1 \pmod{6}, \ 10x \equiv 11 \pmod{13}, \ 3x \equiv 2 \pmod{5},$

(vi) $6x \equiv 3 \pmod{15}, \ 4x \equiv 3 \pmod{17},$

(vii) $2x \equiv 3 \pmod{9}, \ 4x \equiv 2 \pmod{10}, \ x \equiv 4 \pmod{7}.$

2.   Prove: Two simultaneous congruences $x \equiv a \pmod{m}$ and $x \equiv b \pmod{n}$ have a solution if and only if $a \equiv b \pmod{(m, n)}$. If they have a solution, it is unique modulo $[m, n]$.

3.   Find the least two positive integers n such that the remainders when n is divided by 3, 5, and 7 are 2, 3, and 2, respectively.

Additional Topics

1. Application of congruence to calendar problems. Uspensky and Heaslet, p. 206.

2. Number-theoretic functions. Niven and Zuckerman, Chap. 4; Hardy and Wright, Chap. 16; Stewart, Chap. 11; LeVeque [10], Vol. 1, p. 81.

3. Further properties of decimal representations. Hardy and Wright, p. 111 and p. 120.

4. Arithmetical properties of Bernoulli numbers. Uspensky and Heaslet, Chap. 9.

CHAPTER III

POLYNOMIAL CONGRUENCES
AND PRIMITIVE ROOTS

In this chapter we shall continue the study of congruence which was begun in the preceding chapter, with special emphasis on certain questions having to do with solutions of polynomial congruences.

3.1   POLYNOMIAL CONGRUENCES

If $f(x) = \sum_{i=0}^{k} r_i x^i$ and $g(x) = \sum_{i=0}^{k} s_i x^i$ are polynomials with integral co-efficients such that $r_i \equiv s_i \pmod{m}$ for $i = 0, 1, \ldots, k$, we may write

$$f(x) \equiv g(x) \pmod{m}.$$

As an example, we see that

$$5x^3 + 6x^2 + 3x + 7 \equiv x^2 + 3x + 2 \pmod{5}$$

where, as usual, we have omitted writing $0x^3$ on the right.

By writing $f(x) = g(x)$, we shall mean that $r_i = s_i$ for $i = 0, 1, \ldots, k$. If $f(x) = g(x)$, then certainly $f(x) \equiv g(x) \pmod{m}$, but of course the converse need not be true.

In the preceding chapter we wrote $f(x) \equiv 0 \pmod{m}$ to mean that we seek to find integers a such that $f(a) \equiv 0 \pmod{m}$. This is a different use of $\equiv$ from the one introduced here. Although we could use different symbols to indicate these two concepts, we shall follow the usual practice of using the same symbol, with the hope that the context will always make it clear which is intended.

If $f(x) \equiv g(x) \pmod{m}$, it is a consequence of Theorem 2.9 that the congruences $f(x) \equiv 0 \pmod{m}$ and $g(x) \equiv 0 \pmod{m}$ are *equivalent* in the sense that they have exactly the same solutions.

In addition to the familiar concept of the degree of a polynomial, we also need the concept of the degree of a polynomial modulo m.

3.1 DEFINITION. Let $f(x) = \sum_{i=0}^{k} r_i x^i$ be a polynomial with integral coefficients. If $r_n \not\equiv 0 \pmod{m}$, but $r_i \equiv 0 \pmod{m}$ for all values (if there are any) of i such that $n < i \leq k$, we say that $f(x)$ has *degree n modulo m* and that r_n is the *leading coefficient of $f(x)$ modulo m*. If $r_i \equiv 0 \pmod{m}$ for all $i = 0, 1, \ldots, k$, we consider that the polynomial $f(x)$ has *no degree modulo m*.

According to this definition, a polynomial $f(x)$ has no degree modulo m if and only if all of its coefficients are divisible by m.

We may emphasize that the degree of a given polynomial modulo m may very well be different for different moduli m, and may also differ from the degree as defined in elementary algebra. For example, the polynomial

$$12x^4 - 3x^3 + x^2 + x - 2$$

of degree four also has degree four modulo 5, since $12 \not\equiv 0 \pmod{5}$. However, it has degree three modulo 4 and degree two modulo 3.

It is clear that if $f(x)$ has degree n modulo m, there exists a polynomial $g(x)$ of degree n in the usual sense such that $f(x) \equiv g(x) \pmod{m}$. Hence, in considering congruence modulo m we may usually just as well start out by assuming that a given polynomial $f(x)$ of degree n modulo m already has the form $\sum_{i=0}^{n} r_i x^i$, with $r_n \not\equiv 0 \pmod{m}$.

If $f(x)$ is a polynomial of degree n modulo m, it will be convenient to refer to the congruence $f(x) \equiv 0 \pmod{m}$ as a *congruence of degree n.*

Before stating the next result, let us consider the following simple example. Let $f_1(x) = 2x^2 + x + 2$ and $f_2(x) = 3x + 4$. Then $f_1(x)f_2(x) = 6x^3 + 11x^2 + 10x + 8$. Now $f_1(x)$, $f_2(x)$, and $f_1(x)f_2(x)$ have the respective degrees 2, 1, and 2 modulo 6. Clearly, the degree modulo 6 of the product is less than the sum of the degrees modulo 6 of the two factors simply because $2 \cdot 3 \equiv 0 \pmod{6}$ with $2 \not\equiv 0 \pmod{6}$ and $3 \not\equiv 0 \pmod{6}$. This suggests the following simple result whose proof we omit.

3.2 Theorem. *If $f_1(x)$ and $f_2(x)$ have respective degrees n_1 and n_2 modulo m, then $f_1(x)f_2(x)$ cannot have a degree modulo m which exceeds $n_1 + n_2$. If m is a prime, the degree of $f_1(x)f_2(x)$ modulo m is exactly $n_1 + n_2$.*

By the definition of *solution* of a polynomial congruence $f(x) \equiv 0 \pmod{m}$, given in Section 2.5, the number of solutions of such a congruence is the number of incongruent integers which satisfy the congruence. Thus it is the number of integers in a complete residue system modulo m (for example, $\{0, 1, \ldots, m - 1\}$) which satisfy the congruence. As already pointed out, if m is small, it may be easy to find all solutions by inspection. In this way, it is easy to verify that the quadratic congruence $x^2 + 3x + 1 \equiv 0 \pmod{7}$ has no solution, whereas the quadratic congruence $x^2 + 5x \equiv 0 \pmod{6}$ has the four solutions $x \equiv 0, 1, 3, 4 \pmod{6}$. There is no easy way to determine the number of solutions of an arbitrary congruence, but we shall presently establish a few rather special results of some importance. Before proceeding, let us prove the following fundamental theorem.

3.3 Theorem. *If $f(x)$ is a polynomial with integral coefficients and a is an integer, there exists a polynomial $q(x)$ with integral coefficients such that*

3.4 $$f(x) \equiv q(x)(x - a) \pmod{m}$$

if and only if $f(a) \equiv 0 \pmod{m}$.

Proof: If 3.4 holds, it is clear that $f(a) \equiv q(a) \cdot 0 \equiv 0 \pmod{m}$. The converse is an almost immediate consequence of the remainder theorem of elementary algebra. By this theorem, there exists a polynomial $q(x)$ with integral coefficients such that

$$f(x) = q(x)(x - a) + f(a).$$

If $f(a) \equiv 0 \pmod{m}$, it therefore follows at once that $f(x) \equiv q(x)(x-a) \pmod{m}$, and this completes the proof.

3.2   POLYNOMIAL CONGRUENCES MODULO A PRIME

In this section we shall obtain some results which hold when the modulus is restricted to be a prime. Let us first prove the following result.

3.5   THEOREM. *If p is a prime, a polynomial congruence $f(x) \equiv 0$ (mod p) of degree n cannot have more than n solutions.*

PROOF: This result is trivial if $f(x)$ has degree zero modulo p, since such a congruence has *no* solution. Moreover, a congruence of degree 1 modulo p has exactly one solution by Corollary 2.57. We use induction on n and assume that the desired conclusion holds for congruences of degree $n - 1$. If $f(a) \equiv 0$ (mod p), the preceding theorem shows that there exists a polynomial $q(x)$ with integral coefficients such that

$$f(x) \equiv q(x)(x - a) \pmod{p}.$$

If $f(b) \equiv 0$ (mod p), then

$$q(b)(b - a) \equiv 0 \pmod{p}.$$

Hence if $b \not\equiv a$ (mod p), we must have $q(b) \equiv 0$ (mod p). This shows that if $x \equiv b$ (mod p) is a solution of the congruence $f(x) \equiv 0$ (mod p) distinct from the solution $x \equiv a$ (mod p), then $x \equiv b$ (mod p) is also a solution of the congruence $q(x) \equiv 0$ (mod p). Now, by Theorem 3.2, $q(x)$ is of degree $n - 1$ modulo p and, by the induction hypothesis, it cannot have more than $n - 1$ solutions. Accordingly, the congruence $f(x) \equiv 0$ (mod p) cannot have more than n solutions, and the proof is therefore completed.

We observed above that the congruence $x^2 + 5x \equiv 0$ (mod 6) has four solutions. Hence, if the modulus is not a prime, a congruence may have more solutions than its degree.

In the case of a prime modulus p the next theorem characterizes those polynomials $f(x)$ such that the congruence $f(x) \equiv 0$ (mod p) has exactly the same number of solutions as the degree of $f(x)$ modulo p.

3.6   THEOREM. *Let $f(x)$ be a polynomial of positive degree n modulo the prime p. Then the congruence $f(x) \equiv 0$ (mod p) has exactly n solutions if and only if there exists a polynomial $g(x)$ with integral coefficients such that*

3.7 $$x^p - x \equiv g(x)f(x) \pmod{p}.$$

PROOF: Suppose, first, that 3.7 holds and let k be the degree of $g(x)$ modulo p. Then, by Theorem 3.2, we have $k + n = p$. Let s denote the number of solutions of the congruence $g(x) \equiv 0$ (mod p) and t the number of solutions of the congruence $f(x) \equiv 0 \pmod{p}$. By Theorem 3.5, we know that $s \leq k$ and $t \leq n$. However, by 2.37, *every* integer a satisfies the congruence $x^p - x \equiv 0 \pmod{p}$ and therefore also the congruence $g(x)f(x) \equiv 0 \pmod{p}$; that is, this congruence has p solutions. Moreover, since p is a prime, every solution of this last congruence is a solution of at least one of the congruences $g(x) \equiv 0 \pmod{p}$ or $f(x) \equiv 0 \pmod{p}$. Thus we must have $s + t \geq p$. Hence we conclude that $t = n$ (and also $s = k$), since, if $t < n$, it would follow that $s + t < k + n = p$.

Conversely, suppose that the congruence $f(x) \equiv 0 \pmod{p}$ of degree $n > 0$ modulo p has exactly n solutions. Since $f(x)$ is of degree n modulo p, there is no real loss of generality in considering that $f(x) = \sum_{i=0}^{n} r_i x^i$ with $r_n \not\equiv 0 \pmod{p}$. Since $r_n \not\equiv 0 \pmod{p}$, we have $(r_n, p) = 1$ and, by 2.57, there exists an integer c such that $cr_n \equiv 1 \pmod{p}$. If we set $f_1(x) = x^n + \sum_{i=0}^{n-1} cr_i x^i$, we see that $f_1(x) \equiv cf(x) \pmod{p}$ and that $f_1(x)$ has 1 as its leading coefficient. It follows easily that the congruence $f_1(x) \equiv 0 \pmod{p}$ has n solutions, since it has the same solutions as the congruence $f(x) \equiv 0 \pmod{p}$. All of this work has been to get a polynomial with leading coefficient 1 to work with.

Now if we divide the polynomial $x^p - x$ by $f_1(x)$ by the usual method of elementary algebra, we will obtain polynomials $h(x)$ and $r(x)$ *with integral coefficients* such that

$$3.8 \qquad\qquad x^p - x = h(x)f_1(x) + r(x),$$

where $r(x)$ is either the zero polynomial or has degree less than n. If $x \equiv a \pmod{p}$ is any solution of the congruence $f_1(x) \equiv 0 \pmod{p}$, we find that $r(a) \equiv 0 \pmod{p}$, since $a^p - a \equiv 0 \pmod{p}$. That is, the congruence $r(x) \equiv 0 \pmod{p}$ has n solutions, whereas its degree modulo p, if it has a degree modulo p, must be less than n. Hence, by Theorem 3.5, $r(x)$ cannot have a degree modulo p, that is, all of its coefficients are divisible by p. It follows from 3.8 that

$$x^p - x \equiv h(x)f_1(x) \pmod{p}$$

and, since $f_1(x) \equiv cf(x) \pmod{p}$, we conclude that

$$x^p - x \equiv g(x)f(x) \pmod{p},$$

with $g(x) = ch(x)$. This completes the proof of the theorem.

3.9 COROLLARY. *If p is a prime and d is any positive divisor of $p - 1$, the congruence $x^d - 1 \equiv 0 \pmod{p}$ has exactly d solutions.*

Suppose that $p - 1 = dk$. Then

$$x^p - x = x[(x^d)^k - 1] = x(x^d - 1)(x^{d(k-1)} + \cdots + x^d + 1).$$

That is, there exists a polynomial $g(x)$ with integral coefficients such that

$$x^p - x = g(x)(x^d - 1)$$

and hence such that

$$x^p - x \equiv g(x)(x^d - 1) \pmod{p}.$$

The desired result then follows at once from the preceding theorem.

Remark. Let E_a represent the residue class modulo m which contains the integer a. Associated with each polynomial $f(x) = \sum_{i=0}^{k} r_i x^i$ with integral coefficients is the corresponding polynomial $F(x) = \sum_{i=0}^{k} E_{r_i} x^i$ with coefficients in the ring $I/(m)$ of integers modulo m. Moreover, finding a solution of the congruence $f(x) \equiv 0 \pmod{m}$ is equivalent to finding a solution in $I/(m)$ of the equation $F(x) = 0$. Now $I/(p)$ is a field if p is a prime, and an equation with coefficients in a field cannot have more solutions than the degree of the equation. This gives an indication, from a more general point of view, why Theorem 3.5 must be true.

Incidentally, it was pointed out above that the congruence $x^2 + 5x \equiv 0 \pmod{6}$ has the four solutions $x \equiv 0, 1, 3, 4 \pmod{6}$. As an illustration of Theorem 3.3, we may verify that $x^2 + 5x \equiv x(x - 1) \pmod{6}$ and also that $x^2 + 5x \equiv (x - 3)(x - 4) \pmod{6}$. This shows that we do not always have unique factorization of a polynomial into prime (irreducible) polynomials modulo 6. Or, otherwise expressed, a polynomial with coefficients in the ring $I/(6)$ may have more than one factorization into prime polynomials over this ring. Again, such factorization is unique over a *field*, so an essential fact in the above example is that 6 is not a prime.

3.3 POLYNOMIAL CONGRUENCES MODULO A POWER OF A PRIME

It is quite easy to show that the problem of solving arbitrary polynomial congruences can be reduced to the problem of solving polynomial congruences in which the modulus is restricted to be a power of a prime. The situation is clarified in the following theorem.

3.10 THEOREM. *Suppose that the standard form of m is given by* $m = p_1^{k_1} p_2^{k_2} \cdots p_r^{k_r}$. *If* $x \equiv c \pmod{m}$ *is a solution of the polynomial congruence* $f(x) \equiv 0 \pmod{m}$, *then for each* $i = 1, 2, \ldots, r$, *it follows that* $x \equiv c \pmod{p_i^{k_i}}$ *is a solution of the congruence* $f(x) \equiv 0 \pmod{p_i^{k_i}}$. *Conversely, if for each* $i = 1, 2, \ldots, r$, $x \equiv c_i \pmod{p_i^{k_i}}$ *is a solution of the congruence* $f(x) \equiv 0 \pmod{p_i^{k_i}}$, *then there exists exactly one solution* $x \equiv c \pmod{m}$ *of the congruence* $f(x) \equiv 0 \pmod{m}$ *such that* $c \equiv c_i$ $\pmod{p_i^{k_i}}$ *for* $i = 1, 2, \ldots, r$.

PROOF: Clearly, an integer is divisible by m if and only if it is divisible by all $p_i^{k_i}$. Hence $f(c) \equiv 0 \pmod{m}$ if and only if $f(c) \equiv 0 \pmod{p_i^{k_i}}$ for $i = 1, 2, \ldots, r$. The first statement of the theorem follows at once. Moreover, since the different $p_i^{k_i}$ are relatively prime in pairs, the second statement is an immediate consequence of the Chinese Remainder Theorem (2.79).

Using the notation of Theorem 3.10, suppose that the congruence $f(x) \equiv 0 \pmod{p_i^{k_i}}$ has s_i solutions $(i = 1, 2, \ldots, r)$. Then there are s_1 choices of c_1, s_2 choices of c_2, and so on. Hence there are $s_1 s_2 \cdots s_r$ ways of choosing one solution of each of the congruences $f(x) \equiv 0 \pmod{p_i^{k_i}}$. *The congruence* $f(x) \equiv 0 \pmod{m}$ *therefore has precisely* $s_1 s_2 \cdots s_r$ *solutions.* Of course, it has no solution if any s_i is zero.

In view of the preceding theorem, we may concentrate on polynomial congruences of the form $f(x) \equiv 0 \pmod{p^k}$, where p is a prime and k a positive integer. Since $f(a) \equiv 0 \pmod{p^k}$ implies that $f(a) \equiv 0 \pmod{p}$, all integers which satisfy the congruence $f(x) \equiv 0 \pmod{p^k}$ must occur among the integers which satisfy the congruence $f(x) \equiv 0 \pmod{p}$. In general, it may be difficult to determine which of the integers satisfying the latter congruence also satisfy the former. However, one important special case will be presented in the next theorem. Before stating and proving this theorem, we pause to make a few preliminary remarks.

If $f(x) = \sum\limits_{i=0}^{n} r_i x^i$ is a polynomial with integral coefficients, the *derivative* of $f(x)$ is the polynomial $f'(x)$ defined as follows:

$$f'(x) = \sum_{i=1}^{n} i r_i x^{i-1}.$$

Clearly, $f'(x)$ also has integral coefficients. Now suppose that p is a prime, that k is a positive integer, and that c and t are arbitrary integers. We shall prove the following result which will be used in the proof of the theorem below:

3.11 $$f(c + p^k t) \equiv f(c) + f'(c)p^k t \pmod{p^{k+1}}.$$

Using the fact that the binomial coefficients are integers, it follows from the binomial theorem that for each $i > 0$, we have

$$(c + p^k t)^i \equiv c^i + i c^{i-1} p^k t \pmod{p^{k+1}}.$$

Hence

$$f(c + p^k t) \equiv \sum_{i=0}^{n} r_i (c + p^k t)^i \equiv \sum_{i=0}^{n} r_i c^i + \sum_{i=1}^{n} i r_i c^{i-1} p^k t$$
$$\equiv f(c) + f'(c)p^k t \pmod{p^{k+1}},$$

and we have the desired result.

We are now ready to establish the following theorem.

3.12 THEOREM. *Let p be a prime and k an arbitrary positive integer. If $x \equiv a_1 \pmod{p}$ is a solution of the polynomial congruence $f(x) \equiv 0 \pmod{p}$ and if $f'(a_1) \not\equiv 0 \pmod{p}$, then there exists exactly one solution $x \equiv a_k \pmod{p^k}$ of the congruence $f(x) \equiv 0 \pmod{p^k}$ with the property that $a_k \equiv a_1 \pmod{p}$.*

The proof is by induction on k, but we shall merely illustrate the procedure by considering the cases in which $k = 2$ and $k = 3$.

The integers which are congruent to a_1 modulo p are the integers $a_1 + pt$, where t is an integer. We seek to determine for what values of t we will have $f(a_1 + pt) \equiv 0 \pmod{p^2}$. By 3.11 with $c = a_1$ and $k = 1$, we see that

$$f(a_1 + pt) \equiv f(a_1) + f'(a_1)pt \pmod{p^2},$$

and we therefore wish to determine t such that

$$f(a_1) + f'(a_1)pt \equiv 0 \pmod{p^2}.$$

Since $f(a_1) \equiv 0 \pmod{p}$, we may divide throughout by p, and obtain the congruence

$$f'(a_1)t \equiv -\frac{f(a_1)}{p} \pmod{p}.$$

Now since $f'(a_1) \not\equiv 0 \pmod{p}$, this congruence has exactly one solution $t \equiv t_1 \pmod{p}$, and if we set $a_2 = a_1 + pt_1$, it follows that the congruence $f(x) \equiv 0 \pmod{p^2}$ has the unique solution $x \equiv a_2 \pmod{p^2}$ with the property that $a_2 \equiv a_1 \pmod{p}$.

In a similar way we can proceed to the case in which $k = 3$. We have, by 3.11 with $c = a_2$ and $k = 2$, that

$$f(a_2 + p^2t) \equiv f(a_2) + f'(a_2)p^2t \pmod{p^3},$$

and we wish to determine t such that

$$f(a_2) + f'(a_2)p^2t \equiv 0 \pmod{p^3}.$$

Now $f(a_2) \equiv 0 \pmod{p^2}$ and we can therefore divide by p^2 as follows:

$$f'(a_2)t \equiv -\frac{f(a_2)}{p^2} \pmod{p}.$$

Since $a_2 \equiv a_1 \pmod{p}$ and $f'(a_1) \not\equiv 0 \pmod{p}$, it follows that $f'(a_2) \not\equiv 0 \pmod{p}$; hence this congruence has a unique solution $t \equiv t_2 \pmod{p}$. Then if we set $a_3 = a_2 + p^2t_2 = a_1 + pt_1 + p^2t_2$, we see that $x \equiv a_3 \pmod{p^3}$ is the unique solution of the congruence $f(x) \equiv 0 \pmod{p^3}$ with the property that $a_3 \equiv a_1 \pmod{p}$.

The induction procedure is now clear, and we omit further details. Instead, we give an example to illustrate the last two theorems.

Example. Solve the congruence $x^4 + 2x + 36 \equiv 0 \pmod{5^3 \cdot 7}$.

Solution: Let $f(x) = x^4 + 2x + 36$. It is easy to verify that the congruence $f(x) \equiv 0 \pmod 5$ has just one solution $x \equiv -1 \pmod 5$, and that the congruence $f(x) \equiv 0 \pmod 7$ has the two solutions $x \equiv -1 \pmod 7$ and $x \equiv 2 \pmod 7$.

Now $f'(x) = 4x^3 + 2$ and $f'(-1) \not\equiv 0 \pmod 5$, so the preceding theorem assures us that there exists exactly one solution of the congruence $f(x) \equiv 0 \pmod{5^3}$. We proceed to find this solution, using the notation introduced above.

We set $a_1 = -1$. Then

$$f(-1 + 5t) \equiv f(-1) + f'(-1)5t \pmod{5^2},$$

and, using the fact that $f(-1) = 35$ and $f'(-1) = -2$, we have to solve the congruence

$$35 + (-2)5t \equiv 0 \pmod{5^2},$$

or

$$7 - 2t \equiv 0 \pmod 5.$$

The solution is $t \equiv 1 \pmod 5$, so we obtain $a_2 = -1 + 5 = 4$, and $x \equiv 4 \pmod{5^2}$ is the solution of the congruence $f(x) \equiv 0 \pmod{5^2}$.

Similarly, it can be verified that

$$f(4 + 5^2 t) \equiv 0 \pmod{5^3}$$

if and only if $t \equiv 1 \pmod 5$. Accordingly, we have $a_3 = 4 + 5^2 = 29$, and $x \equiv 29 \pmod{5^3}$ is the unique solution of the congruence $f(x) \equiv 0 \pmod{5^3}$.

We are now in a position to use Theorem 3.10 with $m = 5^3 \cdot 7$. In this case, we have only two relatively prime moduli 5^3 and 7, and the Chinese Remainder Theorem is particularly simple. It may be verified that

$$1 = 7 \cdot 18 + (-1) \cdot 125,$$

and hence we have $7 \cdot 18 \equiv 1 \pmod{125}$ and $(-1) \cdot 125 \equiv 1 \pmod 7$. If then we set

$$c = c_1 \cdot 7 \cdot 18 + c_2 \cdot (-1) \cdot 125,$$

it follows that $c \equiv c_1 \pmod{5^3}$ and $c \equiv c_2 \pmod 7$. We thus get all solutions of our given congruence by substituting 29 for c_1 and either -1 or 2 for c_2. Hence the two solutions are

$$x \equiv 29 \cdot 7 \cdot 18 + (-1) \cdot (-1) \cdot 125 \equiv 279 \pmod{5^3 \cdot 7}$$

and

$$x \equiv 29 \cdot 7 \cdot 18 + 2 \cdot (-1) \cdot 125 \equiv 779 \pmod{5^3 \cdot 7}.$$

Exercises

1. Complete the proof of Theorem 3.11 by mathematical induction.

2. Solve each of the following congruences:
   - (i) $x^4 + 3x^3 + 1 \equiv 0 \pmod{5^3}$,
   - (ii) $x^3 + x^2 + 1 \equiv 0 \pmod{3^4}$,
   - (iii) $x^3 + x + 2 \equiv 0 \pmod{5^2 \cdot 7}$,
   - (iv) $x^3 + 5x + 3 \equiv 0 \pmod{7^3}$.
   - (v) $x^2 + 3x + 2 \equiv 0 \pmod{5 \cdot 7 \cdot 11}$,
   - (vi) $x^3 + x + 2 \equiv 0 \pmod{7^2}$.

3. Without actually finding the solutions, determine the number of solutions of each of the following congruences:
   - (i) $x^3 + x^2 + 1 \equiv 0 \pmod{3^7 \cdot 11^{10}}$,
   - (ii) $x^2 - 3 \equiv 0 \pmod{11^4 \cdot 23^2}$.

4. If p is a prime and the congruence $f(x) \equiv 0 \pmod{p}$ is not satisfied by all integers, prove that this congruence is equivalent to a congruence of degree less than p (that is, they have exactly the same solutions). [*Hint:* Consider the remainder in the division of $f(x)$ by $x^p - x$.]

3.4 PRIMITIVE ROOTS

We next continue the study of the concept of the *order* of an integer modulo m, which was begun in Section 2.3. We observed in Corollary 2.40 that if $(a, m) = 1$, the order of a modulo m is a divisor of $\phi(m)$. Hence if m is given, the largest possible order of an integer modulo m is $\phi(m)$. We now make the following convenient definition.

3.13 DEFINITION. *An integer g is said to be a primitive root modulo m if the order of g modulo m is $\phi(m)$.*

In the present terminology, if g is a primitive root modulo m, Corollary 2.42 states that $\{g, g^2, \ldots, g^{\phi(m)}\}$ is a reduced residue system modulo m. It is this property which will be exploited in the following section.

If there exists a primitive root modulo m, it will often be convenient to say that *m has a primitive root.*

It was shown in the examples at the end of Section 2.3 that 14 has a primitive root and that 15 does not have a primitive root. The purpose of this section is to determine those integers m which have primitive roots. First, let us prove the following lemma.

3.14 LEMMA. *If $(m, n) = 1$ with $m > 2$ and $n > 2$, the integer mn does not have a primitive root.*

PROOF: It is easily verified (see Exercise 4, page 42) that both $\phi(m)$ and $\phi(n)$ are even, and it follows that

3.15 $$[\phi(m), \phi(n)] < \phi(m)\phi(n) = \phi(mn).$$

Suppose, now, that $(a, mn) = 1$. Then, $(a, m) = 1$ (and also, of course, $(a, n) = 1$), and Euler's Theorem (2.35) assures us that

$$a^{\phi(m)} \equiv 1 \pmod{m}.$$

If we set $[\phi(m), \phi(n)] = k\phi(m)$, and raise both sides of the preceding congruence to the power k, we conclude that

$$a^{[\phi(m), \phi(n)]} \equiv 1 \pmod{m}.$$

A similar argument shows that also

$$a^{[\phi(m), \ \phi(n)]} \equiv 1 \pmod{n}.$$

It then follows from 2.14 (or as a simple consequence of the fundamental concepts involved) that

$$a^{[\phi(m), \ \phi(n)]} \equiv 1 \pmod{mn}.$$

In view of 3.15, this shows that every integer which is relatively prime to mn has order less than $\phi(mn)$ modulo mn, and the proof is completed.

Let us next prove another negative result as follows:

3.16   LEMMA. *If $k > 2$, then the integer 2^k does not have a primitive root.*

PROOF: Those integers which are relatively prime to 2^k are just the odd integers. If a is an arbitrary odd integer, we shall show that

3.17 $$a^{2^{k-2}} \equiv 1 \pmod{2^k},$$

for every $k > 2$. Since $\phi(2^k) = 2^{k-1}$, this will prove that the order of a modulo 2^k is always less than $\phi(2^k)$ and hence that a cannot be a primitive root modulo 2^k.

Let us therefore prove 3.17. Since a is odd, we have $a = 1 + 2r$ for some integer r. Hence

$$a^2 = (1 + 2r)^2 = 1 + 4r \, (r + 1).$$

Now since one of the two consecutive integers r and $r + 1$ is even, we see that

$$a^2 \equiv 1 \pmod{2^3},$$

which is 3.17 for $k = 3$. We now use induction and show that if 3.17 holds, it also holds with k replaced by $k + 1$. From 3.17, we have that

$$a^{2^{k-2}} = 1 + s \cdot 2^k$$

for some integer s. If we square both sides of this equation, we obtain

$$a^{2^{k-1}} = 1 + s \cdot 2^{k+1} + s^2 \cdot 2^{2k},$$

from which it follows that

$$a^{2^{k-1}} \equiv 1 \pmod{2^{k+1}},$$

and this is just 3.17 with k replaced by $k + 1$. Hence, by induction, 3.17 holds for every integer $k > 2$.

Let us now state the fundamental theorem about primitive roots as follows:

3.18 THEOREM. *An integer* $m > 1$ *has a primitive root if and only if* m *is one of the following:*

$$2, \quad 4, \quad p^k, \quad 2p^k,$$

where p *is an odd prime and* k *an arbitrary positive integer.*

If there exists a primitive root modulo m, Lemma 3.14 shows that m cannot have two distinct odd prime factors and also that it cannot have as factors an odd prime and a power of 2 greater than the first. These facts, together with the result of Lemma 3.16, show that m cannot have a primitive root unless it is of one of the forms specified in the statement of the theorem. Moreover, it is trivial to verify that 1 is a primitive root modulo 2 and that 3 is a primitive root modulo 4. To complete the proof of the theorem we need to show that there does exist a primitive root modulo p^k and $2p^k$. We shall break this part of the proof up into several steps, and first we shall establish the following result.

3.19 LEMMA. *Let* p *be an odd prime and* d *a (positive) divisor of* $p - 1$. *If there exists an integer which has order* d *modulo* p, *then there are exactly* $\phi(d)$ *incongruent integers which have order* d *modulo* p.

PROOF: Suppose that a has order d modulo p. If we let $S = \{a, a^2, \ldots, a^d\}$, the integers in this set are incongruent modulo p by Theorem 2.41. Moreover, Corollary 2.45 shows that among the elements of S there are exactly $\phi(d)$ which have order d modulo p. To complete the proof we only need to show that every integer which has order d modulo p is congruent modulo p to an element of S.

Since a has order d, a satisfies the polynomial congruence

$$x^d \equiv 1 \pmod{p}.$$

Then it is clear that a^t also satisfies this congruence for every positive integer t. In particular, each of the d elements of S satisfies this congruence. Now Corollary 3.9 states that this congruence has exactly d solutions; hence every integer which satisfies the congruence is congruent modulo p to an element of S. The proof is completed by the observation that any integer which has order d modulo p necessarily satisfies this congruence.

3.20   LEMMA. *If p is an odd prime, there exists a primitive root modulo p.*

PROOF: Let R be a reduced residue system modulo p, for example, we may let $R = \{1, 2, \ldots, p - 1\}$. Now, by Corollary 2.40, the order of each element of R modulo p is a divisor of $p - 1$. Suppose that d_1, $d_2, \ldots, d_r$ are all the divisors of $p - 1$, and let us denote by $\psi(d_i)$ the number of elements of R which have order d_i modulo p. It follows that

3.21
$$\sum_{i=1}^{r} \psi(d_i) = p - 1.$$

Moreover, from Theorem 2.31 we know that

3.22
$$\sum_{i=1}^{r} \phi(d_i) = p - 1.$$

Now in the preceding lemma we proved that if $\psi(d_i) \neq 0$, then $\psi(d_i) = \phi(d_i)$. Since always $\phi(d_i) > 0$, it follows that always $\psi(d_i) \neq 0$ since, otherwise, we would have

$$\sum_{i=1}^{r} \psi(d_i) < \sum_{i=1}^{r} \phi(d_i),$$

which is impossible by 3.21 and 3.22. We have therefore proved that if d is any divisor of $p - 1$, there exist $\phi(d)$ elements of R which have order d modulo p. In particular, there are $\phi(p - 1) > 0$ elements of R which are primitive roots modulo p. This shows that every odd prime p has a primitive root.

Now that we have shown the existence of a primitive root modulo p, we proceed to show the existence of a primitive root modulo p^k for an arbitrary positive integer k. To start with, it will be helpful to prove two preliminary results.

3.23   LEMMA. *If p is an odd prime, there exists a primitive root g modulo p such that $g^{p-1} \not\equiv 1 \pmod{p^2}$.*

PROOF: We know, by the preceding lemma, that there exists a primitive root g modulo p. Since $g \equiv g + p \pmod p$, clearly $g + p$ also is a primitive root modulo p. We shall establish the lemma by showing that if $g^{p-1} \equiv 1 \pmod{p^2}$, then $(g + p)^{p-1} \not\equiv 1 \pmod{p^2}$, and therefore either g itself or $g + p$ satisfies the condition stated in the lemma.

Suppose, then, that $g^{p-1} \equiv 1 \pmod{p^2}$. By the binomial theorem, we have

$$(g + p)^{p-1} \equiv g^{p-1} + (p - 1)pg^{p-2} \pmod{p^2}$$

$$\equiv 1 - pg^{p-2} \pmod{p^2}.$$

Since $(g, p) = 1$, it follows that $(g + p)^{p-1} \not\equiv 1 \pmod{p^2}$, thus completing the proof.

The following fact will also be useful in the sequel.

3.24   LEMMA. *Let p be an odd prime. If g is a primitive root modulo p such that $g^{p-1} \not\equiv 1 \pmod{p^2}$, then for each positive integer $k \geq 2$ we have*

3.25 $$g^{p^{k-2}(p-1)} \not\equiv 1 \pmod{p^k}.$$

PROOF: For $k = 2$, it is evident that 3.25 is true by hypothesis. We proceed to prove by induction that it is true for every positive integer $k \geq 2$. It will be sufficient to show that if 3.25 is true, it is also true with k replaced by $k + 1$.

Since $\phi(p^{k-1}) = p^{k-2}(p - 1)$ and $(g, p^{k-1}) = 1$, Euler's Theorem asserts that

$$g^{p^{k-2}(p-1)} \equiv 1 \pmod{p^{k-1}}.$$

Thus there is an integer c such that

3.26 $$g^{p^{k-2}(p-1)} = 1 + cp^{k-1},$$

and 3.25 shows that $(c, p) = 1$. If we raise both sides of Equation 3.26 to the power p, we obtain

$$g^{p^{k-1}(p-1)} \equiv 1 + cp^k \pmod{p^{k+1}}.$$

Since $(c, p) = 1$, this proves that 3.25 holds with k replaced by $k + 1$. We have therefore established the lemma.

We are now ready to prove the following significant fact.

3.27   LEMMA. *There exists an integer g which is a primitive root modulo p^k for each positive integer k.*

PROOF: Let g be an integer, whose existence is asserted by Lemma 3.23, which is a primitive root modulo p and such that $g^{p-1} \not\equiv 1 \pmod{p^2}$. We shall show that such an integer is a primitive root modulo p^k for an arbitrary positive integer k. Clearly, we may assume that $k \geq 2$, since it is given that g is a primitive root modulo p.

Let t be the order of g modulo p^k. The proof will be completed by showing that $t = \phi(p^k) = p^{k-1}(p - 1)$. By Corollary 2.40, we know that $t \mid p^{k-1}(p - 1)$. Moreover, since $g^t \equiv 1 \pmod{p^k}$ implies that $g^t \equiv 1 \pmod{p}$ and g has order $p - 1$ modulo p, the same corollary shows that $(p - 1) \mid t$. Hence we must have $t = p^a(p - 1)$, where $0 \leq a \leq k - 1$. We shall show that the assumption that $a < k - 1$ leads to a contradiction, and hence that we must have $a = k - 1$ and therefore $t = \phi(p^k)$. Suppose, then, that $a \leq k - 2$. If we raise both sides of the congruence

$$g^{p^a(p-1)} \equiv 1 \pmod{p^k}$$

to the power p^{k-2-a}, we obtain

$$g^{p^{k-2}(p-1)} \equiv 1 \pmod{p^k}.$$

However, this violates 3.25 and we have the desired contradiction. This completes the proof of the lemma.

To complete the proof of the theorem, there remains only an easy step as follows.

3.28 LEMMA. *Let g be a primitive root modulo p^k, where p is an odd prime and k a positive integer. Then* (i) *if g is odd, g is also a primitive root modulo $2p^k$,* (ii) *if g is even, $g + p^k$ is a primitive root modulo $2p^k$.*

PROOF: If g is odd, then $g^s \equiv 1 \pmod{2}$ for every positive integer s; hence $g^s \equiv 1 \pmod{2p^k}$ if and only if $g^s \equiv 1 \pmod{p^k}$. It follows that the order of g modulo $2p^k$ is $\phi(p^k)$. However, $\phi(2p^k) = \phi(p^k)$, and this shows that g is a primitive root modulo $2p^k$. If g is even, then $g + p^k$ is odd and we apply the preceding argument to $g + p^k$ which is clearly also a primitive root modulo p^k.

We have at last completed the proof of the theorem. Although we have so far been concerned with questions about the existence of a primitive root modulo m, we can easily say something about the number of primitive roots modulo m. If g is a primitive root modulo m, then $\{g, g^2, \ldots, g^{\phi(m)}\}$ is a reduced residue system modulo m and Corollary 2.45 shows that in this reduced residue system there are exactly $\phi(\phi(m))$ integers which have order $\phi(m)$ modulo m. Thus we have the following result.

3.29 THEOREM. *If there exists a primitive root modulo m, there are precisely $\phi(\phi(m))$ primitive roots modulo m which are incongruent modulo m.*

Table 1 gives the smallest (positive) primitive root g modulo each prime $p < 1000$.

Exercises

In the following, p is always an odd prime.

1.   Verify that 2 is a primitive root modulo 13, and find the least positive residues modulo 13 of all primitive roots modulo 13.

2.   If g is a primitive root modulo p^2, prove that g is a primitive root modulo p.

3.   If g and h are primitive roots modulo p and $g^k \equiv h^l \pmod{p}$, prove that $(k, p - 1) = (l, p - 1)$.

4.   If g is a primitive root modulo p, prove that $g^{(p-1)/2} \equiv -1 \pmod{p}$. Then use this fact to give a new verification of Corollary 2.70 (for an odd prime p).

5.   If g and h are primitive roots modulo p, prove that gh is not a primitive root modulo p.

6.   Prove each of the following:

(i)   If g is a primitive root modulo p and $gh \equiv 1 \pmod{p}$, then h is a primitive root modulo p.

(ii)   If $p > 3$, the product of all (incongruent) primitive roots modulo p is congruent to 1 modulo p.

7.   If g is a primitive root modulo p, prove that there exists an integer h such that $h \equiv g \pmod{p}$ and h is not a primitive root modulo p^2.

8.   Suppose that m_i $(i = 1, 2, \ldots, k)$ are positive integers which are relatively prime in pairs, and that each m_i has a primitive root. Prove that there exists an integer g which is a primitive root modulo every m_i $(i = 1, 2, \ldots, k)$.

9.   Verify that 10 is a primitive root modulo 23. What can you say about the decimal representation of $1/23$?

10.   Describe the decimal representation of $1/1348$. [*Hint:* Use Table 1.]

3.5   INDICES

Throughout this section we shall let q denote a fixed integer which has a primitive root, and let g denote a fixed primitive root modulo q. Moreover, we shall write ϕ for $\phi(q)$. The most important case is that in which $q = p^k$, where p is an odd prime and k is a positive integer. If q is of this form, then $\phi = p^{k-1}(p - 1)$.

Since $\{g, g^2, \ldots, g^{\phi}\}$ is a reduced residue system modulo q and $g^{\phi} \equiv 1 \pmod{q}$, it follows that $\{1, g, \ldots, g^{\phi-1}\}$ also is a reduced residue system modulo q. If a is any integer which is relatively prime to q, there therefore exists a unique integer i with $0 \leq i \leq \phi - 1$ such that $a \equiv g^i \pmod{q}$. Let us make the following definition.

3.30   DEFINITION.   If $(a, q) = 1$, the least nonnegative integer i such that $a \equiv g^i \pmod{q}$ is called the *index* of a (relative to the primitive root g), and we write ind $a = i$.

From the remarks above we see that always $0 \leq$ ind $a \leq \phi - 1$. If we wished to indicate the particular primitive root g which is being used, we could write $\text{ind}_g a$ in place of ind a. However, this is generally not necessary.

Since ind a is defined only if $(a, q) = 1$, when we speak of ind a it is to be assumed that $(a, q) = 1$, whether or not this fact is explicitly mentioned.

The most important properties of indices are stated in the next theorem. The first part follows at once from the fact that $\{1, g, \ldots, g^{\phi-1}\}$ is a reduced residue system modulo q. We leave the proofs of the other two parts to the reader, since they are easy consequences of the definition of index and the fact (Theorem 2.41) that $g^i \equiv g^j \pmod{q}$ if and only if $i \equiv j \pmod{\phi}$.

3.31   THEOREM. *Let q be an integer which has a primitive root and denote $\phi(q)$ by ϕ. Then*

(i)   *ind a = ind b if and only if $a \equiv b \pmod{q}$,*

(ii)   *ind $ab \equiv$ ind a + ind $b \pmod{\phi}$,*

(iii)   *ind $a^n \equiv n$ ind $a \pmod{\phi}$, n a positive integer.*

It has no doubt already been observed that indices are closely analogous to logarithms. Although the concept is mainly of theoretical interest, indices may also be of use in solving congruences of certain types, provided suitable tables of indices are available. In Table 2 we give indices for powers of odd primes which are less than 50. In each case the primitive root which is being used can be identified as the integer with one as an index. We shall illustrate the use of these tables in the following examples.

Example 1. Solve the congruence $14x \equiv 25 \pmod{37}$.

Solution: In this example, $q = 37$ and $\phi = 36$. By Theorem 3.31, the given congruence is satisfied by an integer x if and only if

$$\text{ind } 14 + \text{ind } x \equiv \text{ind } 25 \pmod{36}.$$

From Table 2, we find that ind $14 = 33$ and ind $25 = 10$, so this congruence becomes

$$33 + \text{ind } x \equiv 10 \pmod{36},$$

or ind $x \equiv -23 \pmod{36}$. Thus ind $x = 13$ and, again using the table, we find that $x \equiv 15 \pmod{37}$ is the solution of our given congruence. Of course, this congruence could have been solved by previous methods.

Example 2. Solve the congruence $13x^{18} \equiv 3 \pmod{25}$.

Solution: Since now $q = 25$, we have $\phi = 20$. The given congruence is therefore satisfied by an integer x if and only if

$$\text{ind } 13 + 18 \text{ ind } x \equiv \text{ind } 3 \pmod{20}.$$

The table gives ind $13 = 19$ and ind $3 = 7$. Accordingly, we have

$$19 + 18 \text{ ind } x \equiv 7 \pmod{20},$$

or $18 \text{ ind } x \equiv 8 \pmod{20}$. By the method of Section 2.5, it follows that ind $x = 6$ or ind $x = 16$. From the table we therefore conclude that the given congruence has the two solutions $x \equiv 14 \pmod{25}$ and $x \equiv 11 \pmod{25}$.

Example 3. Solve the congruence $x^6 \equiv 16 \pmod{5^2 \cdot 17 \cdot 23}$.

Solution: Although in this case the modulus does not have a primitive root, we can make use of Theorem 3.10. By use of indices, as in the preceding example, it may be verified that the congruence $x^6 \equiv 16 \pmod{25}$ has the solutions $x \equiv 9 \pmod{25}$ and $x \equiv 16 \pmod{25}$; the congruence $x^6 \equiv 16 \pmod{17}$ has the solutions $x \equiv 4 \pmod{17}$ and $x \equiv 13 \pmod{17}$; and the congruence $x^6 \equiv 16 \pmod{23}$ has the solutions $x \equiv 3 \pmod{23}$ and $x \equiv 20 \pmod{23}$. We proceed to use the Chinese Remainder Theorem (2.79). In the notation used in the proof of that theorem, we let $m_1 = 25$, $m_2 = 17$, and $m_3 = 23$. Then $M_1 = 17 \cdot 23$, $M_2 = 25 \cdot 13$, and $M_3 = 25 \cdot 17$. By solving the appropriate linear congruences, we find that $11M_1 \equiv 1 \pmod{25}$, $-6M_2 \equiv 1 \pmod{17}$, and $-2M_3 \equiv 1 \pmod{23}$. The eight solutions of the given congruence are therefore

$$x \equiv c_1 \cdot 11 \cdot 17 \cdot 23 + c_2(-6) \cdot 25 \cdot 23 + c_3(-2) \cdot 25 \cdot 17 \pmod{5^2 \cdot 17 \cdot 23},$$

with $c_1 = 9$ or 16, $c_2 = 4$ or 13, and $c_3 = 3$ or 20.

Remark. Let G be the group, described at the end of Section 2.5, whose elements are the residue classes E_a modulo m consisting of integers which are relatively prime to m. Then, the statement that m has a primitive root is equivalent to the statement that G is a cyclic group.

In order to use the notation of the present section, let q be an integer which has a primitive root, and let G be the group just described with $m = q$. Let H be the additive group of the integers modulo ϕ, that is, the group whose elements are all the residue classes modulo ϕ with addition as the operation. Then Theorem 3.31 (i) and (ii) show that the mapping $E_a \to E_{\text{ind } a}$, where $(a, q) = 1$, is an isomorphism of the group G onto the group H. This is analogous to the well-known isomorphism $r \to \log r$ of the multiplicative group of the positive real numbers onto the additive group of all real numbers.

We shall next show how the theory of indices can be used to obtain criteria for the existence of solutions of certain polynomial congruences of a particularly simple type. Let us first prove the following result.

3.32 LEMMA. *Let q be an integer which has a primitive root, and set $\phi = \phi(q)$. If $(a, q) = 1$ and n is a positive integer, the congruence*

$$3.33 \qquad\qquad\qquad x^n \equiv a \;(\text{mod } q)$$

has a solution if and only if $(n, \phi)\,|\,\text{ind } a$. If the congruence has a solution, it has exactly (n, ϕ) solutions.

PROOF: Taking indices, we find that the congruence 3.33 is equivalent to the congruence

$$n \text{ ind } x \equiv \text{ind } a \;(\text{mod } \phi).$$

Now, by Theorem 2.55, this linear congruence has a solution if and only if $(n, \phi)\,|\,\text{ind } a$. Moreover, if it has a solution, it has exactly (n, ϕ) solutions. Hence, in this case, there are (n, ϕ) different values for ind x and hence (n, ϕ) values of x which satisfy the congruence 3.33 and are incongruent modulo q. Therefore, the congruence 3.33 has (n, ϕ) solutions, and the proof is completed.

Using this lemma, it is now easy to prove the following important result.

3.34 THEOREM. *Let q be an integer which has a primitive root, and set $\phi = \phi(q)$. If $(a, q) = 1$ and n is a positive integer, then the congruence*

$$x^n \equiv a \;(\text{mod } q)$$

has a solution if and only if

$$a^{\phi/(n,\phi)} \equiv 1 \;(\text{mod } q).$$

If it has a solution, it has exactly (n, ϕ) solutions.

PROOF: Let us set $(n, \phi) = d$, $\phi = \phi_1 d$, so that $\phi/(n, \phi) = \phi_1$. By use of indices, we see that $a^{\phi_1} \equiv 1 \;(\text{mod } q)$ if and only if $\phi_1 \text{ ind } a \equiv 0 \;(\text{mod } \phi_1 d)$, that is, if and only if $d\,|\,\text{ind } a$. The theorem then follows at once from the preceding lemma.

We may point out that Euler's criterion (2.73) is the special case of this theorem in which $n = 2$ and $q = p$, where p is an odd prime. In this case, $\phi = p - 1$ and $(2, p - 1) = 2$.

Exercises

1.   Show that the congruence $x^n \equiv 2 \pmod 7$ has a solution if and only if n is not divisible by 3.

2.   Prove Theorem 3.31 (ii) and (iii).

3.   Use indices and Table 2 to solve each of the following congruences:

   (i) $17x \equiv 12 \pmod{19}$,   (ii) $32x \equiv 15 \pmod{43}$,

   (iii) $15x \equiv 11 \pmod{49}$,   (iv) $x^{20} \equiv 6 \pmod{43}$,

   (v) $3x^{23} \equiv 7 \pmod{13}$,   (vi) $12x \equiv 60 \pmod{69}$,

   (vii) $15x \equiv 7 \pmod{11 \cdot 37}$,   (viii) $x^7 \equiv 5 \pmod{9 \cdot 11 \cdot 13}$.

4.   Determine all integers x such that $10^{x^2} \equiv 11 \pmod{23}$.

5.   Let g and h be primitive roots modulo q and let us denote the index of a relative to g and h by $\text{ind}_g a$ and $\text{ind}_h a$, respectively. Prove that

$$\text{ind}_g a \equiv (\text{ind}_h a)(\text{ind}_g h) \pmod{\phi(q)}.$$

6.   In the notation of this section, verify the following generalization of Corollary 3.9. If $d \mid \phi$, then the congruence $x^d - 1 \equiv 0 \pmod q$ has exactly d solutions.

7.   Let R be a reduced residue system modulo the odd prime p. Apply Theorem 3.34 or use the theory of indices, if you prefer, to prove each of the following:

   (i)   If p is of the form $3k + 2$, the congruence $x^3 \equiv a \pmod p$ has a solution for every element a of R.

   (ii)   If p is of the form $3k + 1$, the congruence $x^3 \equiv a \pmod p$ has a solution for exactly one-third of the elements a of R.

   (iii)   If p is of the form $4k + 3$, the congruence $x^4 \equiv a \pmod p$ has a solution for exactly one-half the elements a of R.

   (iv)   If p is of the form $4k + 1$, the congruence $x^4 \equiv a \pmod p$ has a solution for exactly one-fourth of the elements a of R.

8.   Let q be a number which has a primitive root, and let $R = \{a_1, a_2, \ldots, a_{\phi(q)}\}$ be a reduced residue system modulo q. If, for each positive integer n, we define $R_n = \{a_1^n, a_2^n, \ldots, a_{\phi(q)}^n\}$, prove that R_n is a reduced residue system modulo q if and only if $(n, \phi(q)) = 1$.

9.   Let p be an odd prime. Prove that if there exists an integer a such that $a^4 \equiv -1 \pmod p$, then p must be of the form $8k + 1$.

10.   The preceding exercise shows that every odd prime divisor of $a^4 + 1$ $(a = 1, 2, \ldots)$, is of the form $8k + 1$. Prove that the number of primes of the form $8k + 1$ is infinite. (cf. Theorem 1.39.)

Additional Topics

1.   Primitive λ-roots. Carmichael, p. 71; Ore, p. 292; LeVeque [10], Vol. 1, p. 53.

2.   Indices for a composite modulus. Vinogradov, p. 84 and p. 86; Shanks, p. 111.

CHAPTER IV

QUADRATIC RESIDUES

Certain results obtained in the two preceding chapters give us some information about the solvability of a quadratic congruence of the form $x^2 \equiv a \pmod{p}$, where p is an odd prime and $(a, p) = 1$. The primary purpose of the present short chapter is to go somewhat more deeply into questions of this kind. In particular, we shall prove (4.7) a celebrated theorem of Gauss which is usually called the "law of quadratic reciprocity." This is often considered to be one of the most elegant and significant theorems in the theory of numbers, and it furnishes a powerful tool with which to attack problems of various kinds having to do with the solvability of congruences of the type mentioned above.

4.1 SOME INTRODUCTORY REMARKS

We shall first point out why we may limit ourselves to a consideration of the case in which the modulus is an odd prime. Let m be an arbitrary positive integer greater than 1. The terminology introduced in the following definition will be most convenient.

4.1 DEFINITION. If $(a, m) = 1$, a is said to be a *quadratic residue* of m

if the congruence $x^2 \equiv a \pmod{m}$ has a solution; otherwise, it is a *quadratic nonresidue* of m.

It is clear that if $a \equiv b \pmod{m}$, then a is a quadratic residue of m if and only if b is a quadratic residue of m.

If the standard form of m is given by $m = p_1^{k_1} p_2^{k_2} \cdots p_r^{k_r}$, Theorem 3.10 shows that a (always assumed to be relatively prime to m) is a quadratic residue of m if and only if it is a quadratic residue of each $p_i^{k_i}$ ($i = 1, 2, \ldots, r$). Suppose, now, that p is an odd prime, and let us set $f(x) = x^2 - a$. If $f(a_1) \equiv 0 \pmod{p}$, then $(a_1, p) = 1$ and $f'(a_1) = 2a_1 \not\equiv 0 \pmod{p}$. Hence Theorem 3.12 shows that if p is an odd prime and k an arbitrary positive integer, a is a quadratic residue of p^k if and only if it is a quadratic residue of p. The case of the prime 2 is not covered by these remarks, but it is fairly easy to dispose of it in a quite elementary way. (See Exercise 11 at the end of this chapter.) Accordingly, the problem of determining whether a is a quadratic residue of m essentially reduces to the problem of determining whether a is a quadratic residue of each odd prime factor of m. Throughout the rest of this chapter we shall therefore restrict the modulus to be an odd prime.

Let us next recall from Lemma 2.62 that if p is an odd prime and $(a, p) = 1$, the congruence $x^2 \equiv a \pmod{p}$ either has no solution or has exactly two solutions. This fact will also be an incidental consequence of the remarks to follow. Any integer which satisfies this congruence must be relatively prime to p. Accordingly, the quadratic residues of p are just the integers which are congruent to the squares of the elements of a reduced residue system modulo p. Since $\left\{ -\dfrac{p-1}{2}, \ldots, -2, -1, 1, 2, \ldots, \dfrac{p-1}{2} \right\}$ is one reduced residue system modulo p, the quadratic residues of p are those numbers which are congruent to a number of the set $\left\{ 1^2, 2^2, \ldots, \left(\dfrac{p-1}{2} \right)^2 \right\}$. We leave it to the reader to verify that these $(p-1)/2$ numbers are incongruent modulo p. Hence there exist $(p-1)/2$ incongruent quadratic residues of p. Since each reduced residue system modulo p contains $p-1$ elements, there must also exist the same number, $(p-1)/2$, of incongruent quadratic nonresidues of p. Another method of reaching this same conclusion will be suggested in Exercise 6 below.

4.2   THE LEGENDRE SYMBOL AND A LEMMA OF GAUSS

We next introduce a convenient notation due to Legendre.

4.2   DEFINITION. *If p is an odd prime and $(a, p) = 1$, the Legendre symbol (a/p) is defined as follows:*

$$(a/p) = \begin{cases} 1 \text{ if } a \text{ is a quadratic residue of } p, \\ -1 \text{ if } a \text{ is a quadratic nonresidue of } p. \end{cases}$$

We may emphasize that whether or not it is explicitly mentioned, whenever we use the symbol (a/p), it is to be understood that p is an odd prime and that a is not divisible by p.

Several important properties of the Legendre symbol are collected in the next theorem.

4.3   THEOREM. *Each of the following is true:*

(i) $(a^2/p) = 1$.

(ii)   *If $a \equiv b \pmod{p}$, then $(a/p) = (b/p)$.*

(iii) $(a/p) \equiv a^{(p-1)/2} \pmod{p}$.

(iv) $(ab/p) = (a/p)(b/p)$.

(v) $(-1/p) = (-1)^{(p-1)/2}$.

The first two of these statements are immediate consequences of the definition of the Legendre symbol, and the third is a restatement of Euler's Criterion (2.73). We use part (iii) to prove part (iv) as follows:

$$(ab/p) \equiv (ab)^{(p-1)/2} \equiv a^{(p-1)/2} \cdot b^{(p-1)/2} \equiv (a/p)(b/p) \pmod{p}.$$

Since p is an odd prime and each of (ab/p), (a/p), and (b/p) is ± 1, the congruence $(ab/p) \equiv (a/p)(b/p) \pmod{p}$ implies that $(ab/p) = (a/p)(b/p)$, as required. Finally, part (v) follows from part (iii) by setting $a = -1$.

Let us give an interesting alternate formulation of part (v) of the theorem just proved. Every odd prime is of the form $4n + 1$ or of the form $4n + 3$. If $p = 4n + 1$, then $(p - 1)/2$ is even, and if $p = 4n + 3$, then $(p - 1)/2$ is odd. Accordingly, we see that -1 *is a quadratic residue of every odd prime of the form $4n + 1$, and a quadratic nonresidue of every odd prime of the form $4n + 3$.*

We continue to let p be an odd prime and, for convenience, let us set $h = (p - 1)/2$. Moreover, let us denote by R the reduced residue system modulo p consisting of the residues of least absolute value, that is,

$$R = \{-h, \ldots, -2, -1, 1, 2, \ldots, h\}.$$

Finally, let q be an integer which is relatively prime to p (later on we shall restrict it also to be an odd prime), and let us define the set T as follows:

$$T = \{q, 2q, \ldots, hq\}.$$

Now the elements of T are relatively prime to p and incongruent modulo p; hence each of them is congruent modulo p to exactly one element of R. Using the notation which we have just introduced, we may state as follows an important lemma of Gauss.

4.4 LEMMA. *If n is the number of elements of T which are congruent modulo p to negative elements of R, then $(q/p) = (-1)^n$.*

Before proving this result, let us illustrate it by means of an example. Suppose that $p = 11$ and $q = 7$. In this case, we have

$$R = \{-5, -4, -3, -2, -1, 1, 2, 3, 4, 5\},$$

and

$$T = \{7, 2 \cdot 7, 3 \cdot 7, 4 \cdot 7, 5 \cdot 7\}.$$

The following are easily verified:

$$7 \equiv -4 \pmod{11},$$

$$2 \cdot 7 \equiv 3 \pmod{11},$$

$$3 \cdot 7 \equiv -1 \pmod{11},$$

$$4 \cdot 7 \equiv -5 \pmod{11},$$

$$5 \cdot 7 \equiv 2 \pmod{11}.$$

Hence there are three elements of T which are congruent to negative elements of R, and therefore $n = 3$. The lemma then asserts that $(7/11) = (-1)^3 = -1$, and we may conclude that 7 is not a quadratic residue of 11.

Let us now proceed to prove the lemma. Suppose that $a_1, a_2, \ldots, a_n$ are the negative elements of R which are congruent modulo p to elements of T, and that $b_1, b_2, \ldots, b_m$ are the positive elements of R which are congruent modulo p to elements of T. Clearly, $m + n = h$. Moreover, since the product of all elements of T is $h!q^h$, we conclude that

4.5 $$h!q^h \equiv a_1 a_2 \cdots a_n b_1 b_2 \cdots b_m \pmod{p}.$$

We next observe that we cannot have $-a_i = b_j$, since $a_i + b_j = 0$ would imply that the sum of two elements of T is congruent to zero modulo p, which is impossible (why?). Therefore the set $\{-a_1, -a_2, \ldots, -a_n, b_1, b_2, \ldots, b_m\}$ consists of h distinct positive integers not greater than h, and we must have

4.6 $\{-a_1, -a_2, \ldots, -a_n, b_1, b_2, \ldots, b_m\} = \{1, 2, \ldots, h\}.$

It follows that

$$(-1)^n a_1 a_2 \cdots a_n b_1 b_2 \cdots b_m = h!$$

and, by 4.5, we conclude that

$$(-1)^n h! q^h \equiv h! \pmod{p}.$$

Since $h!$ is relatively prime to p, we can cancel $h!$ from both sides of this congruence and obtain $q^h \equiv (-1)^n \pmod{p}$. Then, by Theorem 4.3 (iii), we see that $(q/p) \equiv (-1)^n \pmod{p}$, and therefore $(q/p) = (-1)^n$. This completes the proof of the lemma.

In the following section we shall make essential use of this lemma in proving the principal theorem about quadratic residues.

4.3   THE LAW OF QUADRATIC RECIPROCITY

In this section we shall establish several preliminary results that will eventually lead to a proof of the following fundamental theorem.

4.7   LAW OF QUADRATIC RECIPROCITY (Gauss). *If p and q are distinct odd primes, then*

$$(p/q)(q/p) = (-1)^{[(p-1)/2] \cdot [(q-1)/2]}.$$

For the present, let us use the notation of the preceding section. In particular, p is an odd prime, $h = (p - 1)/2$, and q is simply an integer which is relatively prime to p. Using the notation $[x]$ for the integral part of x, introduced in Section 1.9, we shall presently find a use for the number M defined as follows:

4.8 $$M = \sum_{i=1}^{h} [iq/p].$$

Now $[iq/p]$ is the quotient in the division of iq by p, and the remainder r_i in this division is the least positive residue of iq modulo p. Thus we have

4.9 $$iq = [iq/p]p + r_i, \qquad 0 < r_i < p.$$

In the notation of the preceding section, if iq is congruent modulo p to a negative element a of R, then the least positive residue of iq modulo p is $p + a$, so that $r_i = p + a$. If iq is congruent modulo p to a positive element b of R, then $r_i = b$. Hence, taking a sum of equations 4.9, we obtain

$$\sum_{i=1}^{h} iq = p \sum_{i=1}^{h} [iq/p] + \sum_{i=1}^{n} (a_i + p) + \sum_{i=1}^{m} b_i.$$

For convenience, let us set

4.10
$$P = \sum_{i=1}^{h} i = \frac{h(h+1)}{2} = \frac{p^2 - 1}{8}.$$

Then the preceding equation reduces to the following:

4.11
$$Pq = pM + np + \sum_{i=1}^{n} a_i + \sum_{i=1}^{m} b_i.$$

However, by 4.6 and 4.10, we have that

$$- \sum_{i=1}^{n} a_i + \sum_{i=1}^{m} b_i = P,$$

and Equation 4.11 can be put in the form

$$Pq = pM + np + P + 2 \sum_{i=1}^{n} a_i,$$

or

4.12
$$P(q - 1) = (M + n)p + 2 \sum_{i=1}^{n} a_i.$$

Now that we have this relation, it is easy to prove the following lemma.

4.13   LEMMA. Let p be an odd prime and let M be defined by 4.8. Then both of the following hold:

(i)   For each odd integer q such that $(p, q) = 1$, we have

$$(q/p) = (-1)^M.$$

(ii) $(2/p) = (-1)^{(p^2-1)/8}.$

If q is odd, then $q - 1 \equiv 0 \pmod 2$, $p \equiv 1 \pmod 2$, and 4.12 implies that $M + n \equiv 0 \pmod 2$. It follows that M and n are both even or they are both odd, and hence that $(-1)^M = (-1)^n$. Part (i) then follows from Lemma 4.4.

If $q = 2$, it follows from the definition of M that $M = 0$, and 4.12 shows that $P \equiv n \pmod 2$. Part (ii) thus also holds by Lemma 4.4.

It is easy to verify that $(p^2 - 1)/8$ is even if p is of the form $8n \pm 1$ and odd if p is of the form $8n \pm 3$. Accordingly, Lemma 4.13 (ii) shows that 2 *is a quadratic residue of every prime of the form* $8n \pm 1$, *and a nonresidue of every prime of the form* $8n \pm 3$.

We now restrict q to be an *odd prime*, so that p and q are therefore distinct odd primes, and let us set $k = (q - 1)/2$. If we interchange the roles of p and q in the above, and set

$$N = \sum_{i=1}^{k} [ip/q],$$

then Lemma 4.13 (i) shows that $(p/q) = (-1)^N$. Hence we have

$$(q/p)(p/q) = (-1)^M \cdot (-1)^N = (-1)^{M+N}.$$

Therefore, in order to prove the reciprocity law (4.7), we only need to show that

$$(-1)^{M+N} = (-1)^{hk},$$

and we shall establish this fact by showing that, in fact,

4.14 $$M + N = hk.$$

We proceed to present a simple geometric proof due to Eisenstein.

In a rectangular coordinate plane, consider the rectangle whose vertices are $(0, 0)$, $(p/2, 0)$, $(p/2, q/2)$, and $(0, q/2)$. By a *lattice point* we mean a point, both of whose coordinates are integers. Since both p and q are odd, the only lattice points on the sides of this rectangle are those on the coordinate axes. We shall establish 4.14 by computing in two different ways the number of lattice points that are *within* the rectangle (not counting those on the sides).

First, we observe that the number of such lattice points is exactly hk since $[p/2] = h$ and $[q/2] = k$.

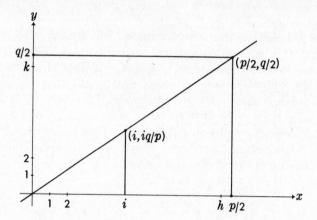

Now let i be a positive integer not greater than h. The diagonal indicated in the figure has equation $y = qx/p$, and the line $x = i$ intersects this diagonal in the point $(i, iq/p)$. Since iq/p is not an integer, we see that among the lattice points within the rectangle none is on the diagonal. Let us count the number below the diagonal. The number of these that are on the line $x = i$ is clearly $[iq/p]$. Hence the number below the diagonal is

$$\sum_{i=1}^{h} [iq/p] = M.$$

A similar calculation will show that the number above the diagonal is N, and we conclude that the total number of lattice points within the rectangle is $M + N$. We showed above that this number is hk, and we have therefore proved 4.14. This completes the proof of the reciprocity law (4.7).

Before illustrating some uses of the result just established, let us state it in a convenient alternative form. Since $(p - 1)/2$ is even or odd according as p is of the form $4n + 1$ or $4n + 3$, we see that the reciprocity law also can be stated as follows.

4.15   LAW OF QUADRATIC RECIPROCITY (Alternate form). *Let p and q be distinct odd primes. Then*

   (i) $(p/q) = (q/p)$ *if at least one of p and q is of the form $4n + 1$,*

   (ii) $(p/q) = -(q/p)$ *if both p and q are of the form $4n + 3$.*

4.4 SOME APPLICATIONS

We now give some examples which will illustrate applications of the reciprocity law in certain types of problems.

Example 1. Determine whether -23 is a quadratic residue or non-residue of 59.

Solution: Our procedure is to compute the value of the Legendre symbol $(-23/59)$. We proceed as follows:

$$(-23/59) = (-1/59)(23/59) \qquad \text{(by 4.3 (iv))}$$
$$= -(23/59) \qquad \text{(by 4.3 (v))}$$
$$= (59/23) \qquad \text{(by 4.15 (ii))}$$
$$= (13/23) \qquad \text{(by 4.3 (ii))}$$
$$= (23/13) \qquad \text{(by 4.15 (i))}$$
$$= (10/13) \qquad \text{(by 4.3 (ii))}$$
$$= (2/13)(5/13) \qquad \text{(by 4.3 (iv))}$$
$$= -(5/13) \qquad \text{(by 4.13 (ii))}$$
$$= -(13/5) \qquad \text{(by 4.15 (i))}$$
$$= -(3/5) \qquad \text{(by 4.3 (ii))}$$
$$= -(-1) = 1.$$

Accordingly, -23 is a quadratic residue of 59.

Example 2. Determine whether 189 is a quadratic residue or non-residue of 313.

Solution: We carry out the calculations and leave it to the reader to supply the reasons. Although 4.3 (i) was not used in the preceding example, it is used at one point here. Since $189 = 3^3 \cdot 7$, we proceed as follows:

$$(189/313) = (3^2/313)(3/313)(7/313)$$
$$= (3/313)(7/313)$$
$$= (313/3)(313/7)$$
$$= (1/3)(5/7) = (5/7)$$
$$= (7/5) = (2/5) = -1.$$

This shows that 189 is a quadratic nonresidue of 313.

Example 3. Show that 3 is a quadratic residue of primes of the form $12n \pm 1$, and a quadratic nonresidue of primes of the form $12n \pm 5$.

Solution: If $p = 12n + r$, where $r = \pm 1, \pm 5$, then $p \equiv 1 \pmod 4$ for $r = 1$ or 5, and $p \equiv 3 \pmod 4$ for $r = -1$ or -5. Hence for $r = 1$ or $r = 5$, we have, by 4.15,

$$(3/p) = (p/3) = (r/3) = \begin{cases} 1 \text{ if } r = 1, \\ -1 \text{ if } r = 5. \end{cases}$$

Similarly, for $r = -1$ or -5, we have

$$(3/p) = -(p/3) = -(r/3) = \begin{cases} 1 \text{ if } r = -1, \\ -1 \text{ if } r = -5. \end{cases}$$

Since $(3/p) = 1$ if p is of the form $12n \pm 1$, and $(3/p) = -1$ if p is of the form $12n \pm 5$, we have thus reached the desired conclusion.

Exercises

1.   Verify the truth of Lemma 4.4 for the case in which $p = 17$ and $q = 2$.

2.   Compute each of the following: $(12/19)$, $(42/47)$, $(15/53)$, $(-20/37)$, $(1000/71)$, $(504/857)$.

3.   Prove that 5 is a quadratic residue of primes of the form $10n \pm 1$ and a quadratic nonresidue of primes of the form $10n \pm 3$.

4.   Prove that -3 is a quadratic residue of the odd prime p if and only if p is of the form $6n + 1$.

5.   Prove that -2 is a quadratic residue of the odd prime p if and only if p is of the form $8n + 1$ or $8n + 3$.

6.   If g is a primitive root modulo the odd prime p, verify that g^r is a quadratic residue of p if and only if r is even. Use this fact to show that p has the same number of (incongruent) quadratic residues as nonresidues.

7.   If p is an odd prime and $ab \equiv r \pmod p$, where r is a quadratic residue of p, prove that a and b are both quadratic residues of p or they are both quadratic nonresidues of p.

8.   If n_1 and n_2 are quadratic nonresidues of the odd prime p, prove that the congruence $n_1 x^2 \equiv n_2 \pmod p$ has a solution.

9.   If p is an odd prime, show that the quadratic congruence

$$ax^2 + bx + c \equiv 0 \pmod p, \qquad\qquad (a, p) = 1,$$

has exactly one solution if $b^2 - 4ac \equiv 0 \pmod p$, has two solutions if $b^2 - 4ac$ is a quadratic residue of p, and has no solution if $b^2 - 4ac$ is a quadratic nonresidue of p. [*Hint:* The given congruence is equivalent to the congruence $(2ax + b)^2 \equiv b^2 - 4ac \pmod p$.]

10.   Prove that the product of the $(p - 1)/2$ incongruent quadratic residues of the odd prime p is congruent modulo p to 1 or -1 according as p is of the form $4n + 3$ or $4n + 1$. [*Hint:* Use Exercise 6 above and Exercise 4, page 80.]

11.   If a is an odd integer, verify each of the following:

(i) a is a quadratic residue of 2.

(ii) a is a quadratic residue of 4 if and only if $a \equiv 1 \pmod 4$.

(iii) a is a quadratic residue of 2^n $(n > 2)$ if and only if $a \equiv 1 \pmod 8$.

[*Hint:* First, prove for $n = 3$. Then use induction as follows: If $k > 2$ and $x_1^2 \equiv a \pmod{2^k}$, it is possible to find t such that $(x_1 + 2^{k-1}t)^2 \equiv a \pmod{2^{k+1}}$.]

12.   Verify that 3 is a quadratic residue of $11^2 \cdot 23$. Without actually finding them, show that the congruence $x^2 \equiv 3 \pmod{11^2 \cdot 23}$ has four solutions.

13.   If p is a prime of the form $2^n + 1$, show that an integer a which is relatively prime to p is a primitive root modulo p if and only if it is a quadratic nonresidue of p.

Additional Topics

1.   The Jacobi symbol (generalizing the Legendre symbol). LeVeque [10], Vol. 1, p. 77; Niven and Zuckerman, p. 71; Uspensky and Heaslet, p. 295.

2.   Sums of two, three, or four squares. Davenport, Chap. 5; Ore, p. 267; Hardy and Wright, Chap. 20; Landau, Part three; Stewart, Chaps. 26 and 27.

3.   Diophantine equations. Ore, Chap. 8; Davenport, Chap. 7; Hardy and Wright, Chap. 13; Uspensky and Heaslet, Chap. 12.

4.   Quadratic forms. Davenport, Chap. 6; Niven and Zuckerman, p. 116; Stewart, Chap. 32.

5.   Algebraic numbers. LeVeque [11], Chap. 6; Niven and Zuckerman, Chap. 9; Hardy and Wright, Chaps. 12, 14, 15.

CHAPTER V

CONTINUED FRACTIONS

The concept of continued fraction, which is to be presented in this chapter, plays an interesting and important role in certain parts of the theory of numbers. After introducing both finite and infinite continued fractions and proving some of their fundamental properties, we consider in detail the (infinite) periodic continued fractions. In particular, we show that the real numbers which have periodic continued fraction expansions are just the quadratic irrationalities. Finally, we give a hint of the usefulness of continued fractions by showing in detail how the periodic continued fraction expansion of $\sqrt{d}$, where d is a positive integer which is not a perfect square, can be applied to the problem of finding all solutions in integers of the so-called Pell's Equation, that is, an equation of the form $x^2 - dy^2 = 1$.

5.1 FINITE CONTINUED FRACTIONS

The following expression is an example of a finite continued fraction:

5.1
$$-3 + \cfrac{1}{2 + \cfrac{1}{4 + \cfrac{1}{5 + \frac{1}{2}}}}.$$

Since expressions of this type are complicated to write or print, it will be helpful to introduce a convenient notation. If n is a nonnegative integer and $x_0, x_1, \ldots, x_n$ are real numbers, all of which are positive except possibly x_0, which is arbitrary, we denote by $\langle x_0, x_1, \ldots, x_n \rangle$ the expression

$$5.2 \qquad x_0 + \cfrac{1}{x_1 + \cfrac{1}{x_2 + \cfrac{}{\ddots \; + \cfrac{1}{x_{n-1} + \cfrac{1}{x_n}}}}}.$$

Such an expression is called a *continued fraction*. The numbers $x_0, x_1, \ldots, x_n$ are called the *terms* or (for a reason to be indicated presently) the *partial quotients* of this continued fraction. Since the continued fraction 5.2 has only the finite number $n + 1$ of terms, it is a *finite* continued fraction. Until Section 5.5 we shall only be considering finite continued fractions and shall sometimes omit the word *finite* and simply speak of continued fractions.

If $a_k (k = 0, 1, \ldots, n)$ are *integers*, we call the continued fraction $\langle a_0, a_1, \ldots, a_n \rangle$ a *simple* continued fraction. We may emphasize that a_0 may be a completely arbitrary integer, but that each a_k with $k > 0$ is to be positive.

In the notation we have here introduced, the continued fraction 5.1 is a simple continued fraction and we may denote it by $\langle -3, 2, 4, 5, 2 \rangle$.

The following formulas, which hold for $n > 0$, follow at once from the definition 5.2 of $\langle x_0, x_1, \ldots, x_n \rangle$, and are of frequent use:

$$5.3 \qquad \langle x_0, x_1, \ldots, x_n \rangle = \left\langle x_0, x_1, \ldots, x_{n-2}, x_{n-1} + \frac{1}{x_n} \right\rangle,$$

$$5.4 \qquad \langle x_0, x_1, \ldots, x_n \rangle = x_0 + \frac{1}{\langle x_1, \ldots, x_n \rangle}.$$

The continued fraction appearing on the right side of 5.3 has n terms. If $n = 1$, it is therefore to be interpreted as $\left\langle x_0 + \dfrac{1}{x_1} \right\rangle = x_0 + \dfrac{1}{x_1}$. A little later on we shall develop a convenient procedure for evaluating a given continued fraction, but first we pause to consider the expansion of a rational number into a simple continued fraction.

5.2   EXPANSION OF A RATIONAL NUMBER

Suppose that r is a given rational number. Thus we may write $r = c/d$, where c and d are integers such that $(c, d) = 1$ and $d > 0$. The Euclidean algorithm, applied to c and d, must yield a unique system of equations of the following form:

$$
\begin{aligned}
c &= a_0 d + r_0, & 0 < r_0 < d, \\
d &= a_1 r_0 + r_1, & 0 < r_1 < r_0, \\
r_0 &= a_2 r_1 + r_2, & 0 < r_2 < r_1, \\
&\quad \cdots\cdots\cdots\cdots & \cdots\cdots\cdots\cdots \\
r_{n-3} &= a_{n-1} r_{n-2} + r_{n-1}, & 0 < r_{n-1} < r_{n-2}, \\
r_{n-2} &= a_n r_{n-1}.
\end{aligned}
$$

5.5

We may observe that in the special case in which $r = c/d$ is an integer (which implies that $d = 1$) there is only one of these equations and in this case $r_0 = 0$. Otherwise, there is more than one equation and $r_{n-1} = 1$ since $(c, d) = 1$. Moreover, $a_n > 1$ since $r_{n-1} < r_{n-2}$. Since c is not required to be positive, we can say nothing about the integer a_0, but all integers occurring in equations after the first are necessarily positive. In particular, $a_1, a_2, \ldots, a_n$ are positive integers.

Let us now rewrite the equations 5.5 as follows:

$$
\begin{aligned}
r = \frac{c}{d} &= a_0 + \frac{r_0}{d} &= a_0 + \frac{1}{d/r_0}, \\
\frac{d}{r_0} &= a_1 + \frac{r_1}{r_0} &= a_1 + \frac{1}{r_0/r_1}, \\
\frac{r_0}{r_1} &= a_2 + \frac{r_2}{r_1} &= a_2 + \frac{1}{r_1/r_2}, \\
&\quad \cdots\cdots\cdots\cdots\cdots\cdots \\
\frac{r_{n-3}}{r_{n-2}} &= a_{n-1} + \frac{r_{n-1}}{r_{n-2}} = a_{n-1} + \frac{1}{r_{n-2}/r_{n-1}}, \\
\frac{r_{n-2}}{r_{n-1}} &= a_n.
\end{aligned}
$$

5.6

If we substitute the expression for d/r_0 given in the second equation into the first, and so on, it follows easily that

5.7
$$
r = \langle a_0, a_1, \ldots, a_n \rangle,
$$

and the rational number r has a representation as a simple continued fraction. We may say also that we have *expanded* r into the simple continued fraction $\langle a_0, a_1, \ldots, a_n \rangle$. The reason for calling the a_i the partial quotients in this continued fraction is now apparent. They are simply the quotients in the successive divisions of the Euclidean algorithm.

We now observe that the representation of a rational number r as a simple continued fraction is not unique. If r is not an integer, then in 5.7 we have $n > 0$ and $a_n > 1$. Since $a_n = (a_n - 1) + 1$ and $a_n - 1$ is a positive integer, we have

5.8 $\qquad r = \langle a_0, a_1, \ldots, a_n \rangle = \langle a_0, a_1, \ldots, a_n - 1, 1 \rangle,$

and hence r has *at least two* representations as a simple continued fraction, one with an even number of partial quotients and the other with an odd number of partial quotients. Moreover, this same conclusion holds also for an arbitrary *integer* r since we clearly have

5.9 $\qquad\qquad\qquad r = \langle r \rangle = \langle r - 1, 1 \rangle.$

Of course, in this case we do not care whether r or $r - 1$ is a positive integer, since the *first* partial quotient in a continued fraction is not required to be positive. Some more precise information is given in the following theorem.

5.10 THEOREM. *A finite simple continued fraction represents c rational number. Conversely, every rational number r has exactly two representations as a finite simple continued fraction, one with an even number of partial quotients and the other with an odd number of partial quotients. If r is an integer, the two representations are given by 5.9. If r is not an integer, the two representations are given by 5.8 (in which $n > 0$ and $a_n > 1$).*

The first sentence is essentially obvious, and so we omit its proof. Moreover, we leave it to the reader to verify that the two representations 5.9 of an *integer* are the only ones. Accordingly, we shall henceforth let r be a rational number which is not an integer. We know that r has the two representations 5.8 as a simple continued fraction, one with the last partial quotient greater than one and the other with the last partial quotient equal to one. The main part of the proof of the theorem will be disposed of by the following lemma.

5.11 LEMMA. *Let r be a rational number which is not an integer. If*

5.12 $\qquad\qquad r = \langle b_0, b_1, \ldots, b_i \rangle = \langle c_0, c_1, \ldots, c_j \rangle,$

where these are simple continued fractions with $b_i > 1$ *and* $c_j > 1$, *then* $i = j$ *and* $b_k = c_k$ ($k = 0, 1, \ldots, i$).

PROOF: By 5.4, we have

5.13 $$r = b_0 + \cfrac{1}{\langle b_1, \ldots, b_i \rangle} = c_0 + \cfrac{1}{\langle c_1, \ldots, c_j \rangle}.$$

Since $i > 0$ and $b_i > 1$, it is clear that $[r] = b_0$, where $[r]$ is the integral part of r. (This is true if $i > 1$ no matter whether $b_i > 1$.) A similar argument shows that $[r] = c_0$; hence $b_0 = c_0$ and Equation 5.13 implies that

5.14 $$\langle b_1, \ldots, b_i \rangle = \langle c_1, \ldots, c_j \rangle.$$

The procedure by which we passed from Equation 5.12 to Equation 5.14 may be repeated if $i > 1$ and $j > 1$, yielding $b_1 = c_1$ and

$$\langle b_2, \ldots, b_i \rangle = \langle c_2, \ldots, c_j \rangle.$$

Suppose, as a matter of notation, that $i \leq j$. By a continuation of the above procedure, we find eventually that $b_k = c_k$ ($k = 0, 1, \ldots, i - 1$) and that

$$\langle b_i \rangle = \langle c_i, \ldots, c_j \rangle.$$

But since $\langle b_i \rangle$ is the integer b_i, and the right side of this equation is not an integer if $i < j$ (since $c_j > 1$), we conclude that $i = j$ and that $b_i = c_i$. The proof of the lemma is therefore completed.

We may interpret this lemma as asserting that the only representation of r as a simple continued fraction in which the last partial quotient is greater than one is the first representation of 5.8. Now if we have a given representation $r = \langle b_0, b_1, \ldots, b_i \rangle$ with $b_i = 1$, we also have the representation $r = \langle b_0, b_1, \ldots, b_{i-1} + 1 \rangle$ and, in view of the fact that $b_{i-1} + 1 > 1$, this last representation must coincide with the first representation of 5.8. It follows that the given representation coincides with second one of 5.8, and this completes the proof of the theorem.

Example. Find the two representations of $77/30$ as a simple continued fraction.

Solution: The Euclidean algorithm yields the following equations:

$$77 = 2 \cdot 30 + 17,$$
$$30 = 1 \cdot 17 + 13,$$
$$17 = 1 \cdot 13 + 4,$$
$$13 = 3 \cdot 4 + 1,$$
$$4 = 4 \cdot 1.$$

Since the successive partial quotients are 2, 1, 1, 3, and 4, we have that

$$77/30 = \langle 2, 1, 1, 3, 4 \rangle.$$

By 5.8, the other representation is as follows:

$$77/30 = \langle 2, 1, 1, 3, 3, 1 \rangle.$$

Exercises

1. Find the two representations of each of the following as a simple continued fraction:

(a) 55/13,   (b) 7/37,   (c) 152/11,
(d) 218/19,   (e) 7/100,   (f) 215/132.

2. If $r = \langle a_0, a_1, \ldots, a_n \rangle$ and $r > 1$, show that $1/r = \langle 0, a_0, a_1, \ldots, a_n \rangle$.

5.3   EVALUATION OF A SIMPLE CONTINUED FRACTION

By straightforward calculation it is easy to verify the following formulas for simple continued fractions with no more than four partial quotients:

$$\langle a_0 \rangle = \frac{a_0}{1},$$

$$\langle a_0, a_1 \rangle = \frac{a_0 a_1 + 1}{a_1},$$

5.15

$$\langle a_0, a_1, a_2 \rangle = \frac{a_0 a_1 a_2 + a_0 + a_2}{a_1 a_2 + 1},$$

$$\langle a_0, a_1, a_2, a_3 \rangle = \frac{a_0 a_1 a_2 a_3 + a_0 a_1 + a_0 a_3 + a_2 a_3 + 1}{a_1 a_2 a_3 + a_1 + a_3}.$$

It seems clear that for a large value of k, a similar explicit expression for $\langle a_0, a_1, \ldots, a_k \rangle$ would be quite complicated. However, we shall soon develop a recursive procedure for evaluating fairly easily a given simple continued fraction. We begin with a few remarks which may at least partially motivate the material to follow.

Let us define p_0, p_1, p_2, p_3 to be the respective numerators of the expressions on the right sides of Equations 5.15; and, similarly, define q_0, q_1, q_2, q_3 to be the respective denominators. Each of the following is then easily verified:

$$p_2 = a_2(a_0a_1 + 1) + a_0 = a_2p_1 + p_0,$$

$$q_2 = a_2a_1 + 1 = a_2q_1 + q_0.$$

Similarly, the following may be verified:

$$p_3 = a_3p_2 + p_1,$$

$$q_3 = a_3q_2 + q_1.$$

Thus, for $k = 2$ or 3, we have $\langle a_0, a_1, \ldots, a_k \rangle = p_k/q_k$ with

$$p_k = a_kp_{k-1} + p_{k-2},$$

$$q_k = a_kq_{k-1} + q_{k-2}.$$

Actually, this statement also holds for $k = 0$ or 1 if we define (somewhat artificially, but conveniently) $p_{-2} = 0$, $p_{-1} = 1$, $q_{-2} = 1$, $q_{-1} = 0$. For, under these definitions, each of the following would be true:

$$p_0 = a_0 = a_0p_{-1} + p_{-2},$$

$$q_0 = 1 = a_0q_{-1} + q_{-2},$$

$$p_1 = a_1a_0 + 1 = a_1p_0 + p_{-1},$$

$$q_1 = a_1 = a_1q_0 + q_{-1}.$$

These observations for $k = 0, 1, 2, 3$ will soon be generalized to arbitrary k. However, we find it helpful to make the following change in viewpoint. Let $a_0, a_1, a_2, \ldots$ be an infinite sequence of integers, all of them positive except possibly a_0. We now define sequences $\{p_k\}$ and $\{q_k\}$ of integers in a recursive way as follows:

5.16
$$p_{-2} = 0, \; p_{-1} = 1, \; p_k = a_kp_{k-1} + p_{k-2}, \qquad (k = 0, 1, 2, \ldots),$$

$$q_{-2} = 1, \; q_{-1} = 0, \; q_k = a_kq_{k-1} + q_{k-2}, \qquad (k = 0, 1, 2, \ldots).$$

For later reference, let us observe that since $q_{-1} = 0$, the (possibly zero or negative) integer a_0 does not occur in the formula for q_0 and hence that $q_k > 0$ for every $k \geq 0$. Moreover, since a_k is a positive integer for $k > 0$, we see that

$$0 < q_0 \leq q_1 < q_2 < q_3 \cdots .$$

In particular, we must have

5.17 $q_k \geq k$ $(k = 0, 1, 2, \ldots).$

We shall now prove the following result which will be much used throughout the rest of this chapter.

5.18   THEOREM. *Let* a_0, a_1, a_2, $\ldots$ *be an infinite sequence of integers, all positive except possibly* a_0, *and let integers* p_k *and* q_k *be defined by 5.16. Then for each positive real number* x *and for each nonnegative integer* k, *we have*

5.19 $\langle a_0, a_1, \ldots, a_{k-1}, x \rangle = \dfrac{xp_{k-1} + p_{k-2}}{xq_{k-1} + q_{k-2}}.$

It is to be understood that the continued fraction on the left side of 5.19 has $k + 1$ terms, so that it is to be interpreted as $\langle x \rangle$ if $k = 0$.

The proof is by induction on k. For $k = 0$, we have

$$\frac{xp_{-1} + p_{-2}}{xq_{-1} + q_{-2}} = \frac{x}{1} = \langle x \rangle,$$

and 5.19 is true for $k = 0$. To complete the proof, let us assume that 5.19 holds for some k (for every positive real number x), and show that the corresponding result holds for $k + 1$. Using 5.3 and the induction hypothesis, we find that

$$\langle a_0, a_1, \ldots, a_k, x \rangle = \left\langle a_0, a_1, \ldots, a_{k-1}, a_k + \frac{1}{x} \right\rangle$$

$$= \frac{\left(a_k + \dfrac{1}{x} \right) p_{k-1} + p_{k-2}}{\left(a_k + \dfrac{1}{x} \right) q_{k-1} + q_{k-2}}$$

$$= \frac{x(a_k p_{k-1} + p_{k-2}) + p_{k-1}}{x(a_k q_{k-1} + q_{k-2}) + q_{k-1}}$$

$$= \frac{xp_k + p_{k-1}}{xq_k + q_{k-1}} \qquad \text{(by 5.16)}.$$

This verifies that 5.19 holds with k replaced by $k + 1$, and the proof is therefore completed.

The following result, which generalizes our observations above, is obtained from this theorem by replacing x in 5.19 by a_k and using the definition 5.16 of p_k and q_k.

5.20   COROLLARY. *For each nonnegative integer k, we have*

$$\langle a_0, a_1, \ldots, a_k \rangle = \frac{p_k}{q_k}.$$

Since p_k and q_k depend only on $a_0, a_1, \ldots, a_k$, it is clear that we do not in fact need to consider an *infinite* sequence a_k in order to evaluate a finite simple continued fraction. Let us illustrate how the preceding corollary, together with 5.16, makes it fairly easy to evaluate a given continued fraction. For example, let us evaluate $\langle -3, 2, 4, 5, 2 \rangle$, which was introduced in 5.1 as our first example of a continued fraction. The calculations are indicated by the following convenient table. The values of $a_0, a_1, a_2, a_3,$ and a_4 are exhibited in the second row of the table. After the values of $p_{-2}, p_{-1}, q_{-2},$ and q_{-1} have been inserted

k	-2	-1	0	1	2	3	4
a_k			-3	2	4	5	2
p_k	0	1	-3	-5	-23	-120	-263
q_k	1	0	1	2	9	47	103

(and they *always* have the values here indicated), the values of all the remaining p's are successively computed by the formula $p_k = a_k p_{k-1} + p_{k-2}$; and similarly for the q's. Then by Corollary 5.20, we have that

$$\langle -3, 2, 4, 5, 2 \rangle = \frac{p_4}{q_4} = -\frac{263}{103}.$$

Let us now prove a few important general properties of sequences $\{p_k\}$ and $\{q_k\}$ defined by 5.16. First, we shall prove the following result.

5.21   THEOREM. *For each integer $k \geq -1$, we have*

5.22 $$p_k q_{k-1} - p_{k-1} q_k = (-1)^{k-1}.$$

The proof is by induction. The cases in which $k = -1$ or $k = 0$ are not very important, but they are easily verified by direct calculation. Moreover,

$$p_1q_0 - p_0q_1 = (a_1a_0 + 1) \cdot 1 - a_0a_1 = 1,$$

and it follows that 5.22 holds for $k = 1$. Let us then assume that k is such that 5.22 holds and verify the corresponding result for $k + 1$. Thus we have

$$\begin{aligned}
p_{k+1}q_k - p_kq_{k+1} &= (a_{k+1}p_k + p_{k-1})q_k - p_k(a_{k+1}q_k + q_{k-1}) \\
&= -(p_kq_{k-1} - p_{k-1}q_k) \\
&= -(-1)^{k-1} = (-1)^k.
\end{aligned}$$

This shows that 5.22 holds with k replaced by $k + 1$, and the proof is therefore completed.

Equation 5.22 shows that 1 is expressible as a linear combination of p_k and q_k. In particular, we have the following important result.

5.23 COROLLARY. *For each integer $k \geq 0$, p_k and q_k are relatively prime.*

Another result of some importance which follows quite easily from Theorem 5.21 is the following.

5.24 COROLLARY. *For each nonnegative integer k, we have*

5.25 $$p_kq_{k-2} - p_{k-2}q_k = (-1)^ka_k.$$

To prove this, we observe that

$$\begin{aligned}
p_kq_{k-2} - p_{k-2}q_k &= (a_kp_{k-1} + p_{k-2})q_{k-2} - p_{k-2}(a_kq_{k-1} + q_{k-2}) \\
&= a_k(p_{k-1}q_{k-2} - p_{k-2}q_{k-1}) = (-1)^{k-2}a_k,
\end{aligned}$$

by 5.22. Since $(-1)^{k-2} = (-1)^k$, we have the desired result.

If he has not already done so, it may be instructive for the reader to verify the truth of 5.22 and 5.25 for the numerical example given in the table above (for $k \leq 4$).

5.4 THE EQUATION $cx + dy = 1$

If c and d are relatively prime integers, the equations of the Euclidean algorithm have been frequently used to express 1 as a linear combination of c and d. We now observe that these calculations can be carried out in a routine manner by using the procedure of the preceding section.

Suppose that c and d are relatively prime and that d (at least) is positive. Then the Equations 5.5 of the Euclidean algorithm show that

$c/d = \langle a_0, a_1, \ldots, a_n \rangle$. By Corollary 5.20, we have $c/d = p_n/q_n$. Moreover, since $(c, d) = 1$, $(p_n, q_n) = 1$, $d > 0$, and $q_n > 0$, we conclude that $c = p_n$ and $d = q_n$. Then, by Theorem 5.22, we have

$$cq_{n-1} - p_{n-1}d = (-1)^{n-1}.$$

Thus, if n is odd, the equation $cx + dy = 1$ has a solution $x = q_{n-1}$, $y = -p_{n-1}$. If n is even, we have a solution $x = -q_{n-1}$, $y = p_{n-1}$. Of course, we know by Theorem 5.10 that we may make n even or odd as we wish. Moreover, after one solution of the equation $cx + dy = 1$ has been found, all solutions may be found by applying Theorem 1.20.

Example. Find a solution of the equation $312x + 53y = 1$.

Solution: By the preceding remarks, it is clear that we begin by expressing $312/53$ (or $53/312$) as a simple continued fraction. The Euclidean algorithm gives rise to the following equations:

$$312 = 5 \cdot 53 + 47,$$
$$53 = 1 \cdot 47 + 6,$$
$$47 = 7 \cdot 6 + 5,$$
$$6 = 1 \cdot 5 + 1,$$
$$5 = 5 \cdot 1.$$

Hence, $312/53 = \langle 5, 1, 7, 1, 5 \rangle$, and we compute the table below by the method of the example of the preceding section.

k	-2	-1	0	1	2	3	4
a_k			5	1	7	1	5
p_k	0	1	5	6	47	53	312
q_k	1	0	1	1	8	9	53

Since $n = 4$ is even, we have that $x = -9$, $y = 53$ is a solution of the given equation. As indicated above, we could also express $312/53$ as a continued fraction with $n = 5$.

If two integers are given, it may not be obvious whether or not they are relatively prime until the calculations of the Euclidean algorithm have been carried out. The procedure described above may be used to express the g.c.d. of two integers as a linear combination of the two integers—even if they are not relatively prime. Suppose that $(r, s) = t$ with $s > 0$. If $r = ct$, $s = dt$, it may be verified that the *quotients* in the Euclidean algorithm as applied to r and s coincide with the corresponding quotients in the Euclidean algorithm as applied to c and d (the other integers appearing are all multiplied by t). If these quotients are $a_0, a_1, \ldots, a_n$, we then have

$$\frac{r}{s} = \frac{c}{d} = \langle a_0, a_1, \ldots, a_n \rangle.$$

Moreover, the equation $cq_{n-1} - p_{n-1}d = (-1)^{n-1}$ yields, upon multiplication by t, the equation

$$rq_{n-1} - p_{n-1}s = (-1)^{n-1}t.$$

Let us illustrate these observations by another example.

Example. Express the g.c.d. of 561 and 171 as a linear combination of these two integers.

Solution: The equations of the Euclidean algorithm are as follows:

$$561 = 3 \cdot 171 + 48,$$
$$171 = 3 \cdot 48 + 27,$$
$$48 = 1 \cdot 27 + 21,$$
$$27 = 1 \cdot 21 + 6,$$
$$21 = 3 \cdot 6 + 3,$$
$$6 = 2 \cdot 3.$$

These equations show that $(561, 171) = 3$, and also that

$$\frac{561}{171} = \frac{187}{57} = \langle 3, 3, 1, 1, 3, 2 \rangle.$$

We continue by constructing the following table as in the preceding example.

k	-2	-1	0	1	2	3	4	5
a_k			3	3	1	1	3	2
p_k	0	1	3	10	13	23	82	187
q_k	1	0	1	3	4	7	25	57

It follows that $25 \cdot 187 - 82 \cdot 57 = 1$, and our calculations therefore show that $25 \cdot 561 - 82 \cdot 171 = 3$.

Exercises

1. Evaluate each of the following continued fractions:

   (a) $\langle 1, 2, 3, 4, 2 \rangle$,   (b) $\langle -1, 2, 1, 2, 3, 4 \rangle$,

   (c) $\langle 2, 2, 2, 2, 2, 2 \rangle$,   (d) $\langle 1, 2, 1, 2, 1, 2, 1 \rangle$.

2. Use the method of this section to find a solution of each of the following equations:

   (a) $16x + 117y = 1$,   (b) $144x + 11y = 1$,

   (c) $13x + 19y = 1$,   (d) $54x + 23y = 1$,

   (e) $48x - 91y = 1$,   (f) $17x - 13y = 1$.

3. Express the g.c.d. of each of the following pairs of integers as a linear combination of the two integers:

   (a) 354 and 231,   (b) 572 and 363,

   (c) 2064 and 473,   (d) 2681 and 1134.

4. In the notation of 5.16, show that

   $$q_k/q_{k-1} = \langle a_k, a_{k-1}, \ldots, a_1 \rangle, \qquad\qquad (k = 1, 2, \ldots).$$

5. In the notation of 5.16, if $a_0 > 0$ show that

   $$p_k/p_{k-1} = \langle a_k, a_{k-1}, \ldots, a_0 \rangle, \qquad\qquad (k = 0, 1, 2, \ldots).$$

5.5 INFINITE CONTINUED FRACTIONS

Suppose that $a_0, a_1, a_2, \ldots$ is a given infinite sequence of integers, all positive except possibly a_0, and let sequences $\{p_k\}$ and $\{q_k\}$ be defined as in 5.16. It will be convenient to set

$$c_k = \langle a_0, a_1, \ldots, a_k \rangle$$

for each nonnegative integer k and to call these c_k *convergents* (of an infinite continued fraction to be defined presently). More precisely, c_k may be called the kth convergent, and we may also call c_k an even or an odd convergent according as k is even or odd. We may observe that c_k is a finite continued fraction with $k + 1$ terms.

For our purposes, it is of fundamental importance that, by Corollary 5.20,

5.26 $$c_k = \frac{p_k}{q_k}, \qquad\qquad (k = 0, 1, 2, \ldots).$$

We shall presently prove that $\lim_{k \to \infty} c_k$ always exists. Some important steps in the argument will be furnished by the following theorem.

5.27 THEOREM. (i) *The even convergents form a strictly increasing sequence, that is,*

$$c_0 < c_2 < c_4 < \cdots .$$

(ii) *The odd convergents form a strictly decreasing sequence, that is,*

$$c_1 > c_3 > c_5 > \cdots .$$

(iii) *Every odd convergent is greater than every even convergent.*

Proof of (i): For each *even* $k \geq 2$, Equation 5.25 may be written in the form

$$\frac{p_k}{q_k} = \frac{p_{k-2}}{q_{k-2}} + \frac{a_k}{q_{k-2}q_k},$$

or, in view of 5.26,

$$c_k = c_{k-2} + \frac{a_k}{q_{k-2}q_k}.$$

Since the q's are all positive and also $a_k > 0$ (since $k > 0$), we conclude that $c_{k-2} < c_k$, as we wished to show.

Proof of (ii): For each *odd* $k \geq 3$, we find in a similar way by use of 5.25 that

$$c_{k-2} = c_k + \frac{a_k}{q_{k-2}q_k},$$

and therefore that $c_{k-2} > c_k$.

Proof of (iii): First, let us observe that if t is a nonnegative integer, from 5.22 with $k = 2t + 1$, we find that

$$\frac{p_{2t+1}}{q_{2t+1}} - \frac{p_{2t}}{q_{2t}} = \frac{1}{q_{2t+1}q_{2t}}$$

or

5.28 $$c_{2t+1} = c_{2t} + \frac{1}{q_{2t+1}q_{2t}}.$$

Certainly, then,

5.29 $$c_{2t+1} > c_{2t}.$$

Now let r and s be arbitrary nonnegative integers and let us establish part (iii) of the theorem by showing that $c_{2r+1} > c_{2s}$.

If $r = s$, we have the desired result by 5.29.

If $r > s$, then 5.29 (with $t = r$) and part (i) of the present theorem show that

$$c_{2r+1} > c_{2r} > c_{2s}.$$

Similarly, if $r < s$, using part (ii) of the present theorem, we find that

$$c_{2r+1} > c_{2s+1} > c_{2s}.$$

Hence, in every case, $c_{2r+1} > c_{2s}$, and this completes the proof of the theorem.

We may now easily establish the following result.

5.30   THEOREM. *If a_0, a_1, a_2, ... is an infinite sequence of integers, all positive except possibly a_0, and if $c_k = \langle a_0, a_1, \ldots, a_k \rangle$, then $\lim_{k \to \infty} c_k$ always exists. Moreover, if r and s are any nonnegative integers, it follows that $c_{2r} < \lim_{k \to \infty} c_k < c_{2s+1}$.*

PROOF: By Theorem 5.27 (i) and (iii) the sequence $\{c_{2k}\}$ is an increasing sequence which is bounded by any odd convergent, and therefore $\lim_{k \to \infty} c_{2k}$ exists and is greater than each even convergent. In like manner, using Theorem 5.27 (ii) and (iii), we know that $\lim_{k \to \infty} c_{2k+1}$ exists and is less than each odd convergent. Moreover, from Equation 5.28, we have

$$\lim_{k \to \infty} c_{2k+1} = \lim_{k \to \infty} c_{2k} + \lim_{k \to \infty} \frac{1}{q_{2k+1} q_{2k}}.$$

However, 5.17 implies that this last limit is zero, and we conclude that

$$\lim_{k \to \infty} c_{2k+1} = \lim_{k \to \infty} c_{2k}.$$

We have shown that the sequence of odd convergents has the same limit as the sequence of even convergents, and this implies that

$$\lim_{k \to \infty} c_k = \lim_{k \to \infty} c_{2k} = \lim_{k \to \infty} c_{2k+1}.$$

Thus $\lim_{k \to \infty} c_k$ exists, and the first two sentences of the proof show that it satisfies the desired inequality.

In view of this theorem, we now make the following definition.

5.31   DEFINITION. We say that an infinite sequence a_0, a_1, a_2, ... of integers, all positive except possibly a_0, defines an *infinite simple con-*

tinued fraction $\langle a_0, a_1, a_2, \ldots \rangle$ whose value is defined as follows:

$$\langle a_0, a_1, a_2, \ldots \rangle = \lim_{k \to \infty} c_k,$$

where $c_k = \langle a_0, a_1, \ldots, a_k \rangle$. Moreover, for each nonnegative integer k, a_k is called a *partial quotient* and $c_k = \langle a_0, a_1, \ldots, a_k \rangle$ a *convergent* of this infinite simple continued fraction.

Since the only infinite continued fractions which we shall consider are simple (that is, the partial quotients are integers), we shall henceforth omit the word "simple" and call them infinite continued fractions.

Let us next prove the following result.

5.32   LEMMA. *If* $\alpha = \langle a_0, a_1, a_2, \ldots \rangle$, *then* $[\alpha] = a_0$ *and*

5.33
$$\alpha = a_0 + \frac{1}{\langle a_1, a_2, \ldots \rangle}.$$

PROOF: By the second statement of Theorem 5.30 (with $r = s = 0$), we see that

$$a_0 < \alpha < a_0 + \frac{1}{a_1}.$$

Since $a_1 \geq 1$, it follows that

5.34
$$a_0 < \alpha < a_0 + 1$$

and hence that $[\alpha] = a_0$. Moreover, for $k > 0$ we have

$$c_k = \langle a_0, a_1, \ldots, a_k \rangle = a_0 + \frac{1}{\langle a_1, a_2, \ldots, a_k \rangle}$$

so that

$$\alpha = \lim_{k \to \infty} c_k = a_0 + \frac{1}{\lim_{k \to \infty} \langle a_1, a_2, \ldots, a_k \rangle},$$

and this is precisely 5.33 by definition of the infinite continued fraction $\langle a_1, a_2, \ldots \rangle$.

We are now ready to prove that two distinct infinite continued fractions have different values. We state this result in the following form.

5.35   THEOREM. *If* $\langle a_0, a_1, \ldots \rangle$ *and* $\langle b_0, b_1, \ldots \rangle$ *are infinite continued fractions such that*

5.36 $\langle a_0, a_1, \ldots \rangle = \langle b_0, b_1, \ldots \rangle,$

then $a_k = b_k$ *for every nonnegative integer* k.

This result is easily proved by induction on k. By the preceding lemma, we have

$$a_0 + \frac{1}{\langle a_1, a_2, \ldots \rangle} = b_0 + \frac{1}{\langle b_1, b_2, \ldots \rangle}.$$

Moreover, a_0 is the integral part of $\langle a_0, a_1, \ldots \rangle$ and b_0 is the integral part of $\langle b_0, b_1, \ldots \rangle$, so that we must have $a_0 = b_0$. The preceding equation then shows that

$$\langle a_1, a_2, \ldots \rangle = \langle b_1, b_2, \ldots \rangle.$$

A repetition of the argument by which we obtained this equation from 5.36 will show that $a_1 = b_1$ and that

$$\langle a_2, a_3, \ldots \rangle = \langle b_2, b_3, \ldots \rangle.$$

It is almost obvious how to complete the proof by induction, and we leave the details to the reader.

We showed in Section 5.2 that every rational number can be represented (in two ways) as a finite simple continued fraction. The following result may therefore not be surprising.

5.37   THEOREM. *The value of every infinite continued fraction is an irrational number.*

PROOF: Let $\alpha = \langle a_0, a_1, a_2, \ldots \rangle$ and let us assume that α is rational and seek a contradiction. By 5.34, we see that the value of an infinite continued fraction cannot be an integer. Accordingly, by our assumption and Theorem 5.10, α can be expressed as a finite simple continued fraction $\langle b_0, b_1, \ldots, b_n \rangle$ with $n > 0$ and $b_n > 1$. Thus we have

5.38 $\alpha = \langle a_0, a_1, a_2, \ldots \rangle = \langle b_0, b_1, \ldots, b_n \rangle.$

Now by the proof of Lemma 5.11, $[\alpha] = b_0$; and, by Lemma 5.32, $[\alpha] = a_0$. Moreover, by 5.4 and 5.33, we have

$$a_0 + \frac{1}{\langle a_1, a_2, \ldots \rangle} = b_0 + \frac{1}{\langle b_1, \ldots, b_n \rangle}.$$

Since $a_0 = b_0$, we conclude that

$$\langle a_1, a_2, \ldots \rangle = \langle b_1, b_2, \ldots, b_n \rangle.$$

In exactly the same way as we passed from 5.38 to this equation, if $n > 1$ we may conclude that

$$\langle a_2, a_3, \ldots \rangle = \langle b_2, \ldots, b_n \rangle.$$

A repetition of this argument (cf. the proof of Lemma 5.11), will lead to an equation

$$\langle a_n, a_{n+1}, \ldots \rangle = \langle b_n \rangle.$$

Now the right side of this equation is the integer b_n and the left side is an infinite continued fraction. However, this is impossible, since we have already observed that the value of an infinite continued fraction cannot be an integer. We have therefore obtained the desired contradiction, and the theorem is established.

5.6 EXPANSION OF AN IRRATIONAL NUMBER

We showed in the preceding section that the value of every infinite continued fraction is an irrational number. In this section we consider the problem of finding an infinite continued fraction which represents a given irrational number in the sense that its value is the given irrational number.

Let α be a given irrational number which, for notational convenience, we shall also denote by α_0. Let $a_0 = [\alpha]$, so that a_0 is the integral part of α_0. Then, since α_0 is irrational, we have $0 < \alpha_0 - a_0 < 1$. We now define $\alpha_1 = 1/(\alpha_0 - a_0)$ and observe that α_1 is irrational, since α_0 is irrational, and that $\alpha_1 > 1$. We may remark that the equation defining α_1 may also be written in the form

$$\alpha_0 = a_0 + \frac{1}{\alpha_1},$$

which is perhaps more appropriate for our purposes. We may now define an irrational number α_2 in terms of α_1 in the same way that α_1 was defined in terms of α_0. In general, by recursion, we define an infinite sequence $\{\alpha_k\}$ as follows, in which we use the notation $a_k = [\alpha_k]$:

5.39 $$\alpha_0 = \alpha, \quad \alpha_{k-1} = a_{k-1} + \frac{1}{\alpha_k}, \qquad (k = 1, 2, \ldots).$$

Now α_{k-1} an irrational number implies that α_k is irrational; hence by induction all α_k are irrational. Thus, for each positive integer k we must have $0 < \alpha_{k-1} - a_{k-1} < 1$, and we see that $\alpha_k > 1$ and hence that

$a_k > 0$ for every $k > 0$. Obviously, a_0 need not necessarily be positive.

For a fixed positive integer k, the Equations 5.39 which define α_1, $\alpha_2, \ldots, \alpha_k$ may be written in the following explicit form:

$$\alpha = \alpha_0 = a_0 + \frac{1}{\alpha_1},$$

$$\alpha_1 = a_1 + \frac{1}{\alpha_2},$$

5.40 $$\alpha_2 = a_2 + \frac{1}{\alpha_3},$$

$$\cdots\cdots\cdots\cdots\cdots$$

$$\alpha_{k-1} = a_{k-1} + \frac{1}{\alpha_k}.$$

If in the first of these equations we replace α_1 by the expression for α_1 in the second equation, then make a similar substitution for α_2 from the third equation, and so on, we find the important fact that for each nonnegative integer k,

5.41 $$\alpha = \langle a_0, a_1, \ldots, a_{k-1}, \alpha_k \rangle.$$

Since every a_k is an integer and $a_k > 0$ for $k > 0$, by Definition 5.31 we may consider the infinite continued fraction $\langle a_0, a_1, a_2, \ldots \rangle$. As perhaps at least partially suggested by 5.41, we shall now prove the following result.

5.42   THEOREM. *Let α be an irrational number and let $a_k = [\alpha_k]$, where the numbers α_k are defined by 5.39. Then*

$$\alpha = \langle a_0, a_1, a_2, \ldots \rangle.$$

PROOF: Let us define sequences $\{p_k\}$ and $\{q_k\}$ as in 5.16. Then by 5.19 and 5.41, we have that for each nonnegative integer k,

5.43 $$\alpha = \frac{\alpha_k p_{k-1} + p_{k-2}}{\alpha_k q_{k-1} + q_{k-2}}.$$

As in the preceding section, let

$$c_k = \langle a_0, a_1, \ldots, a_k \rangle = \frac{p_k}{q_k}, \qquad (k = 0, 1, 2, \ldots).$$

Now for each integer $k \geq 2$, we have

$$\alpha - c_{k-1} = \alpha - \frac{p_{k-1}}{q_{k-1}} = \frac{\alpha_k p_{k-1} + p_{k-2}}{\alpha_k q_{k-1} + q_{k-2}} - \frac{p_{k-1}}{q_{k-1}}$$

$$= \frac{p_{k-2}q_{k-1} - p_{k-1}q_{k-2}}{q_{k-1}(\alpha_k q_{k-1} + q_{k-2})}$$

$$= \frac{(-1)^{k-1}}{q_{k-1}(\alpha_k q_{k-1} + q_{k-2})} \qquad \text{(by 5.22)}.$$

Since $\alpha_k > 1$ and all q's are positive integers, it follows at once that

$$|\alpha - c_{k+1}| < \frac{1}{q_{k-1}^2} \qquad (k = 2, 3, \ldots).$$

Since, by 5.17, $q_{k-1} \geq k - 1$, we conclude that $\lim_{k \to \infty} c_k = \alpha$, and thus that $\alpha = \langle a_0, a_1, a_2, \ldots \rangle$, by Definition 5.31. This completes the proof of the theorem.

Theorems 5.35, 5.37, and 5.42 show that there exists a one-one correspondence between the set of all infinite continued fractions and the set of all irrational numbers.

It is worth pointing out that if we should apply the above procedure to find the infinite continued fraction expansion of α_k (rather than of $\alpha = \alpha_0$), we would just be starting at a later point in the recursive process defined by 5.39. Let us state this fact more precisely as the following lemma.

5.44   Lemma. *For each α_k (defined as in 5.39), we have*

$$\alpha_k = \langle a_k, a_{k+1}, a_{k+2}, \ldots \rangle.$$

It will be recalled that the integers a_i are called *partial quotients* of the infinite continued fraction $\langle a_0, a_1, a_2, \ldots \rangle$. It is also customary to give a name to the α_k introduced above, as follows:

5.45   Definition. The numbers α_k, defined as in 5.39, may be called the *complete quotients* of the infinite continued fraction $\langle a_0, a_1, a_2, \ldots \rangle$.

By the preceding lemma, each complete quotient α_k is represented by an infinite continued fraction which is obtained from the given continued fraction $\langle a_0, a_1, a_2, \ldots \rangle$ by simply starting with the partial quotient a_k rather than with a_0.

For later use, let us point out the following result.

5.46   LEMMA. *Let β be an irrational number greater than 1, and suppose that $\beta = \langle b_0, b_1, b_2, \ldots \rangle$. If n is a positive integer and $a_0, a_1, \ldots, a_{n-1}$ are integers, all of which are positive except possibly a_0, then*

$$5.47 \quad \langle a_0, a_1, \ldots, a_{n-1}, \beta \rangle = \langle a_0, a_1, \ldots, a_{n-1}, b_0, b_1, b_2, \ldots \rangle.$$

PROOF: We observe first that $b_0 > 0$, since $\beta > 1$ and $b_0 = [\beta]$. Therefore, the right side of 5.47 is indeed an infinite continued fraction. If we let $\alpha = \langle a_0, a_1, \ldots, a_{n-1}, b_0, b_1, b_2, \ldots \rangle$, and define the α_k as in 5.39, it follows from Lemma 5.44 and the fact that the representation of α as an infinite continued fraction is unique that $\alpha_n = \langle b_0, b_1, b_2, \ldots \rangle = \beta$. Then 5.41 shows that $\alpha = \langle a_0, a_1, \ldots, a_{n-1}, \beta \rangle$, and this completes the proof of the lemma.

We next give an example to illustrate the finding of the representation of a given irrational number as an infinite continued fraction. We may also say that we are finding the infinite continued fraction expansion of a given irrational number.

Example. Expand $\sqrt{3}$ into an infinite continued fraction.

Solution: Let us set $\alpha_0 = \sqrt{3}$ and compute the first few partial quotients and complete quotients, using 5.39 (or 5.40). These calculations are exhibited below.

$$a_0 = [\sqrt{3}] = 1, \ \sqrt{3} = 1 + \frac{1}{\alpha_1}, \ \alpha_1 = \frac{1}{\sqrt{3}-1} = \frac{\sqrt{3}+1}{2},$$

$$a_1 = \left[\frac{\sqrt{3}+1}{2}\right] = 1, \ \frac{\sqrt{3}+1}{2} = 1 + \frac{1}{\alpha_2}, \ \alpha_2 = \frac{2}{\sqrt{3}-1} = \sqrt{3}+1,$$

$$a_2 = [\sqrt{3}+1] = 2, \ \sqrt{3}+1 = 2 + \frac{1}{\alpha_3}, \ \alpha_3 = \frac{1}{\sqrt{3}-1} = \alpha_1.$$

Since the complete quotient α_3 is equal to the complete quotient α_1, the calculations clearly repeat and we obtain

$$\sqrt{3} = \langle 1, 1, 2, 1, 2, 1, 2, \ldots \rangle$$

with the block 1, 2 repeating indefinitely. This is usually written in the simple form

$$\sqrt{3} = \langle 1, \overline{1, 2} \rangle,$$

and we say that the infinite continued fraction expansion of $\sqrt{3}$ is *periodic*. Later on, we shall discuss periodic continued fractions in some detail.

Exercises

1. Compute the first six convergents in the infinite continued fraction expansion of $\sqrt{3}$ and use them to illustrate Theorem 5.27.

2. Find the infinite continued fraction expansion of $\sqrt{6}$.

3. If α is a real number greater than one, and $\alpha = \langle a_0, a_1, a_2, \dots \rangle$, show that $1/\alpha = \langle 0, a_0, a_1, \dots \rangle$. Use this fact to prove that for each positive integer k, the kth convergent for $1/\alpha$ is the reciprocal of the $(k-1)$th convergent for α.

5.7 APPROXIMATION BY RATIONAL NUMBERS

Let α be a given irrational number and let its infinite continued fraction representation be given by $\alpha = \langle a_0, a_1, a_2, \dots \rangle$. In our previous notation (in particular, in Section 5.5), we know from Theorems 5.27 and 5.30 that the even convergents $c_{2k} = p_{2k}/q_{2k}$ form a strictly increasing sequence and that they are all less than α, whereas the odd convergents $c_{2k+1} = p_{2k+1}/q_{2k+1}$ form a strictly decreasing sequence and they are all greater than α. Actually, each convergent is nearer to α than the preceding convergent. Let us state this result as follows:

5.48 THEOREM. *If* $\alpha = \langle a_0, a_1, a_2, \dots \rangle$, *and sequences* $\{p_k\}$ *and* $\{q_k\}$ *are defined in the usual way by 5.16, then for each positive integer n we have*

$$\left| \alpha - \frac{p_n}{q_n} \right| < \left| \alpha - \frac{p_{n-1}}{q_{n-1}} \right|.$$

PROOF: By 5.41, we have that

$$\alpha = \langle a_0, a_1, \dots, a_n, \alpha_{n+1} \rangle,$$

where α_{n+1} denotes the appropriate complete quotient according to the notation of the preceding section. It follows from 5.19 that

$$\alpha = \frac{\alpha_{n+1} p_n + p_{n-1}}{\alpha_{n+1} q_n + q_{n-1}},$$

which may be written in the form

$$\alpha_{n+1}(\alpha q_n - p_n) = -\alpha q_{n-1} + p_{n-1}$$

$$= -q_{n-1}\left(\alpha - \frac{p_{n-1}}{q_{n-1}} \right).$$

Now, dividing by $\alpha_{n+1}q_n$, we find that

$$\alpha - \frac{p_n}{q_n} = -\frac{q_{n-1}}{\alpha_{n+1}q_n}\left(\alpha - \frac{p_{n-1}}{q_{n-1}}\right).$$

Since $\alpha_{n+1} > 1$ and $q_n \geq q_{n-1}$, it follows from this equation that

$$\left|\alpha - \frac{p_n}{q_n}\right| < \left|\alpha - \frac{p_{n-1}}{q_{n-1}}\right|,$$

and the proof is completed.

The sequence $c_0, c_1, c_2, \ldots$ of convergents is a sequence of rational numbers, each of which we may consider as an approximation to the irrational number α. Not only is it true that $\alpha = \lim_{k\to\infty} c_k$, but the theorem just proved shows that $c_0, c_1, c_2, \ldots$ is a sequence of successively closer approximations to α. The next theorem shows that $c_n = p_n/q_n$ is, in fact, the *best* approximation to α among all the rational numbers with denominators not exceeding q_n. A precise statement of this fact is the following.

5.49   Theorem. *Let p_n/q_n be the nth convergent to the infinite continued fraction representing the irrational number α. If c and d are integers with $d > 0$ and $(c, d) = 1$ such that*

$$\left|\alpha - \frac{c}{d}\right| < \left|\alpha - \frac{p_n}{q_n}\right|, \qquad\qquad n > 0,$$

then $d > q_n$.

Proof: Of the two successive convergents p_{n-1}/q_{n-1} and p_n/q_n, one is even and the other is odd, and hence α lies between them. Moreover, the preceding theorem shows that α is nearer to p_n/q_n than to p_{n-1}/q_{n-1}. The hypothesis of the present theorem then implies that c/d lies between p_{n-1}/q_{n-1} and p_n/q_n, and hence that

$$\left|\frac{p_n}{q_n} - \frac{p_{n-1}}{q_{n-1}}\right| > \left|\frac{c}{d} - \frac{p_{n-1}}{q_{n-1}}\right|.$$

But the q's are all positive and $|p_nq_{n-1} - p_{n-1}q_n| = 1$, so we have that

$$\frac{1}{q_nq_{n-1}} > \left|\frac{cq_{n-1} - dp_{n-1}}{dq_{n-1}}\right|,$$

or

$$\frac{1}{q_n} > \frac{|cq_{n-1} - dp_{n-1}|}{d}.$$

In turn, this implies that

$$d > q_n |cq_{n-1} - dp_{n-1}|.$$

Clearly, $cq_{n-1} - dp_{n-1} \neq 0$ since, otherwise, it would follow that $c/d = p_{n-1}/q_{n-1}$ and our hypothesis would contradict the preceding theorem. Hence $|cq_{n-1} - dp_{n-1}|$ is a positive integer and $d > q_n$, as we wished to show.

In order to give an example illustrating this theorem, we would need to consider the infinite continued fraction representation of some irrational number. In general, it may be difficult or impossible to exhibit in any simple explicit way this infinite continued fraction. However, it is easy to find the first few partial quotients if a sufficiently good decimal approximation of the irrational number is known. In this way, it may be shown that the first four partial quotients for the irrational number π are 3, 7, 15, 1. Let us compute the first few numbers p_k and q_k as indicated in the following table.

k	-2	-1	0	1	2	3
a_k			3	7	15	1
p_k	0	1	3	22	333	355
q_k	1	0	1	7	106	113

It follows that the convergents

$$\frac{3}{1}, \ \frac{22}{7}, \ \frac{333}{106}, \ \frac{355}{113}$$

are successively less than π and greater than π. Moreover, 22/7 approximates π more closely than any rational number (in lowest terms) with denominator not exceeding 7. Similarly, 333/106 and 355/113 are better approximations to π than any rational number with denominator not exceeding 106 or 113, respectively.

For later use, we now prove the following result.

5.50   Theorem. *Let α be an irrational number. If c and d are integers with $d > 0$ and $(c, d) = 1$ such that*

5.51

$$\left| \alpha - \frac{c}{d} \right| < \frac{1}{2d^2},$$

then c/d is one of the convergents in the infinite continued fraction representation of α.

PROOF: We first expand the rational number c/d into a finite simple continued fraction as follows:

5.52 $$\frac{c}{d} = \langle a_0, a_1, \ldots, a_n \rangle.$$

By Theorem 5.10, we may choose n to be either even or odd and we use this freedom of choice as follows. *If α > c/d, we choose n to be even; and if α < c/d, we choose n to be odd.* The proof of the theorem will consist in showing that the infinite continued fraction expansion of $α$ has $a_0, a_1, \ldots, a_n$ as its first $n + 1$ partial quotients.

Let us dispose of the case in which $n = 0$ since this case is essentially trivial. In view of our choice of n, this case occurs only if $α > c/d$ and $d = 1$, since $c/d = \langle a_0 \rangle$. The hypothesis of the theorem then implies that $0 < α - c/d < 1/2$ and hence that $[α] = c/d$. It follows that c/d is the *first* convergent in the infinite continued fraction representation of $α$. Henceforth in the proof we shall assume that $n > 0$.

As usual, let us denote the convergents of $\langle a_0, a_1, \ldots, a_n \rangle$ by p_k/q_k ($k = 0, 1, \ldots, n$) so that, in particular, $p_n/q_n = c/d$. In fact, $c = p_n$ and $d = q_n$ (why?). We next *define* a number $β$, necessarily irrational, by the following equation:

5.53 $$α = \frac{βp_n + p_{n-1}}{βq_n + q_{n-1}}.$$

The main part of the proof of the theorem consists in showing that $β > 1$. For the moment, let us assume this fact as known and point out how the rest of the proof goes. Since $β > 0$, we may consider the finite continued fraction $\langle a_0, a_1, \ldots, a_n, β \rangle$ and, by 5.53 and 5.19, it follows that

$$α = \langle a_0, a_1, \ldots, a_n, β \rangle.$$

Let $β = \langle b_0, b_1, b_2, \ldots \rangle$ be the infinite continued fraction representation of $β$. Since $β > 1$, Lemma 5.46 shows that

$$α = \langle a_0, a_1, \ldots, a_n, b_0, b_1, b_2, \ldots \rangle$$

and therefore $c/d = \langle a_0, a_1, \ldots, a_n \rangle$ is indeed a convergent in the infinite continued fraction representation of $α$.

There remains to prove that $β > 1$. By solving Equation 5.53 for $β$, we obtain

5.54 $$\beta = \frac{p_{n-1} - \alpha q_{n-1}}{\alpha q_n - p_n} = \frac{q_{n-1}}{q_n} \cdot \frac{p_{n-1}/q_{n-1} - \alpha}{\alpha - p_n/q_n}.$$

In view of Theorem 5.21 and the fact that $0 < q_{n-1} \leq q_n$, we have that

$$\left| \frac{p_n}{q_n} - \frac{p_{n-1}}{q_{n-1}} \right| = \frac{1}{q_{n-1}q_n} \geq \frac{1}{q_n^2}.$$

Accordingly, since $c = p_n$ and $d = q_n$, we see from 5.51 that

5.55 $$2\left| \alpha - \frac{p_n}{q_n} \right| < \left| \frac{p_n}{q_n} - \frac{p_{n-1}}{q_{n-1}} \right|.$$

We first show that $\beta > 0$, and make the argument in two cases as follows:

Case 1. $\alpha > c/d = p_n/q_n$, n even. Then, by Theorem 5.27, we have

$$\frac{p_n}{q_n} < \frac{p_{n-1}}{q_{n-1}}.$$

Hence in this case, 5.55 becomes

$$2\left(\alpha - \frac{p_n}{q_n} \right) < \frac{p_{n-1}}{q_{n-1}} - \frac{p_n}{q_n},$$

and it follows that

$$0 < \alpha - \frac{p_n}{q_n} < \frac{p_{n-1}}{q_{n-1}} - \alpha,$$

and 5.54 shows that $\beta > 0$.

Case 2. $\alpha < c/d = p_n/q_n$, n odd. Then

$$\frac{p_{n-1}}{q_{n-1}} < \frac{p_n}{q_n},$$

and 5.55 becomes

$$2\left(\frac{p_n}{q_n} - \alpha \right) < \frac{p_n}{q_n} - \frac{p_{n-1}}{q_{n-1}}.$$

It now follows that

$$0 < \frac{p_n}{q_n} - \alpha < \alpha - \frac{p_{n-1}}{q_{n-1}},$$

and again $\beta > 0$.

We shall now show that, in fact, $\beta > 1$. If we write

$$\frac{p_{n-1}}{q_{n-1}} - \frac{p_n}{q_n} = \left(\frac{p_{n-1}}{q_{n-1}} - \alpha\right) + \left(\alpha - \frac{p_n}{q_n}\right),$$

we see that

$$\frac{1}{q_{n-1}q_n} = \left|\frac{p_{n-1}}{q_{n-1}} - \frac{p_n}{q_n}\right| \leq \left|\frac{p_{n-1}}{q_{n-1}} - \alpha\right| + \left|\alpha - \frac{p_n}{q_n}\right|,$$

and, using 5.51, it follows that

$$\left|\frac{p_{n-1}}{q_{n-1}} - \alpha\right| > \frac{1}{q_{n-1}q_n} - \frac{1}{2q_n^2} \geq \frac{1}{q_{n-1}q_n} - \frac{1}{2q_{n-1}q_n} = \frac{1}{2q_{n-1}q_n}.$$

Hence, from 5.54 and 5.51, we conclude that

$$\beta = |\beta| > \frac{q_{n-1}}{q_n} \cdot \frac{\dfrac{1}{2q_{n-1}q_n}}{|\alpha - p_n/q_n|} = \frac{1}{2q_n^2 |\alpha - p_n/q_n|} > 1.$$

This completes the proof of the theorem.

5.8   QUADRATIC IRRATIONALITIES

In this section we pause to introduce and briefly discuss a concept whose relevance to the subject of continued fractions will be brought out in the following section.

We begin with the following definition.

5.56   DEFINITION. A real number is called a *quadratic irrationality* if it is expressible in the form $u + v\sqrt{d}$, where u and v are rational numbers with $v \neq 0$, and d is a positive integer which is not a perfect square.

Now let R be the set of all rational numbers and let d be a positive integer which is not a perfect square. It will be convenient to define a set $R(\sqrt{d})$ as follows:

$$R(\sqrt{d}) = \{u + v\sqrt{d}; u, v \in R\}.$$

The irrational elements of $R(\sqrt{d})$ are those elements $u + v\sqrt{d}$ with $v \neq 0$ and they are therefore quadratic irrationalities by the preceding definition.

If α and β are elements of $R(\sqrt{d})$, it is easy to verify that each of the following is an element of $R(\sqrt{d})$:

$$\alpha \pm \beta, \quad \alpha\beta, \quad \alpha/\beta \text{ if } \beta \neq 0.$$

Such a set of numbers is usually called a *field*, so we shall speak of the field $R(\sqrt{d})$. Of course, R itself is a field which is contained in the field $R(\sqrt{d})$.

We may point out that the elements of $R(\sqrt{d})$ are *uniquely* expressible in the form $u + v\sqrt{d}$, where $u, v \in R$. For if

$$u_1 + v_1 \sqrt{d} = u_2 + v_2 \sqrt{d},$$

it follows that

$$(v_1 - v_2) \sqrt{d} = u_2 - u_1.$$

Hence we must have $v_1 = v_2$, and therefore also $u_1 = u_2$, since otherwise $\sqrt{d}$ would be equal to the rational number $(u_2 - u_1)/(v_1 - v_2)$.

5.57   Definition. If $\alpha = u + v\sqrt{d} \in R(\sqrt{d})$, then the element α' of $R(\sqrt{d})$ defined by $\alpha' = u - v\sqrt{d}$ is called the *conjugate* of α.

It is obvious that if α' is the conjugate of α, then also α is the conjugate of α'. This fact may be expressed by the equation $(\alpha')' = \alpha$. Clearly, also, $\alpha = \alpha'$ if and only if $v = 0$, that is, if and only if $\alpha \in R$. Therefore, if α is a quadratic irrationality, α' also is a quadratic irrationality and $\alpha \neq \alpha'$.

We leave it to the reader to verify the following important properties in which α and β are elements of $R(\sqrt{d})$:

5.58
(i) $(\alpha \pm \beta)' = \alpha' \pm \beta'$,
(ii) $(\alpha\beta)' = \alpha'\beta'$,
(iii) $(\alpha/\beta)' = \alpha'/\beta'$, $\qquad\qquad\qquad\qquad\qquad\qquad \beta \neq 0$.

Remark: The mapping $\alpha \to \alpha' (\alpha \in R(\sqrt{d}))$ is a one-one mapping of the field $R(\sqrt{d})$ onto itself. Moreover, addition and multiplication are preserved under this mapping (as stated in 5.58 (i) and (ii)). That is, it is an isomorphism of $R(\sqrt{d})$ onto itself. Another way of stating this fact is to say that it is an *automorphism* of $R(\sqrt{d})$.

Using 5.58 and the fact that a rational number is equal to its conjugate, it is easy to establish the following result to which we shall want to make explicit reference in the following section. We shall leave the proof as an exercise.

5.59 LEMMA. *If $\beta \in R(\sqrt{d})$ and*

$$\gamma = \frac{\beta w_1 + w_2}{\beta w_3 + w_4}, \qquad \qquad \beta w_3 + w_4 \neq 0,$$

where the w's are rational numbers, then

$$\gamma' = \frac{\beta' w_1 + w_2}{\beta' w_3 + w_4}.$$

Next, let us observe that if $\alpha = u + v\sqrt{d}$ with $v \neq 0$, then α and α' are the two distinct roots of the quadratic equation

$$x^2 - 2ux + u^2 - dv^2 = 0.$$

Clearly, the coefficients of this equation are rational numbers.

Let us now change the point of view as follows. Suppose that α is a quadratic irrationality and that $f(x) = ax^2 + bx + c$ is a quadratic polynomial with rational coefficients such that $f(\alpha) = 0$. By use of 5.58 (i) and (ii), it follows that

$$0 = 0' = (a\alpha^2 + b\alpha + c)' = a\alpha'^2 + b\alpha' + c = f(\alpha').$$

Thus we have shown that if the quadratic irrationality α is a root of a quadratic equation with rational coefficients, the other root is necessarily α'.

We conclude this section by establishing the following result.

5.60 LEMMA. *Every quadratic irrationality α may be expressed in the form*

$$\alpha = \frac{\sqrt{d} + r}{s},$$

where d is a positive integer which is not a perfect square and r and s are integers with $s \neq 0$ such that $s \mid (d - r^2)$.

PROOF: Our hypothesis implies that $\alpha = u + v\sqrt{d}$, where u and v are rational numbers with $v \neq 0$. Clearly, then, we may write

$$\alpha = \frac{a + b\sqrt{d}}{c},$$

where a, b, and c are *integers* with $b \neq 0$ and $c \neq 0$. It follows that

$$\alpha = \frac{a \pm \sqrt{b^2 d}}{c}$$

and $b^2 d$ is not a perfect square, since d is not a perfect square. For simplicity, we shall now write d_1 in place of $b^2 d$. Moreover, by possibly changing the signs of a and c, we can always have the $+$ sign before the radical. Thus we obtain

$$\alpha = \frac{a + \sqrt{d_1}}{c} = \frac{a \cdot |c| + \sqrt{c^2 d_1}}{c \cdot |c|} = \frac{a_1 + \sqrt{d_2}}{c_1},$$

where $a_1 = a \cdot |c|$, $c_1 = c \cdot |c|$, and $d_2 = c^2 d_1$. Then d_2 is a positive integer which is not a perfect square. Moreover,

$$d_2 - a_1^2 = c^2 d_1 - a^2 c^2 = c^2 (d_1 - a^2),$$

and it follows that $c_1 \mid (d_2 - a_1^2)$. The proof is now completed by making an obvious change in notation.

5.9   PERIODIC CONTINUED FRACTIONS

As an example in Section 5.6, we showed that the continued fraction expansion of $\sqrt{3}$ is periodic. More precisely, we found that

$$\sqrt{3} = \langle 1, 1, 2, 1, 2, 1, 2, \ldots \rangle,$$

with the terms 1, 2 repeating indefinitely. We usually write this as $\sqrt{3} = \langle 1, \overline{1, 2} \rangle$ and say that this continued fraction has the *period* 1, 2 and that the period begins after one term.

In general, a *periodic continued fraction* is one of the form

5.61 $\langle b_0\ b_1, \ldots, b_{n-1}, \overline{c_0, c_1, \ldots, c_{m-1}} \rangle$

for some nonnegative integer n and some positive integer m. As. to notation, we shall consider that there are no b's appearing in 5.61 if $n = 0$. This is merely to let this case be included in the general form 5.61. In 5.61, we shall assume that n and m are chosen as small as possible. We may then say that $c_0, c_1, \ldots, c_{m-1}$ is the *period* (of length m) and that the period begins after n terms. If $n = 0$, we have a *purely periodic* continued fraction.

It is not difficult to find the value of a given periodic continued fraction. As an example, let us compute the value of $\beta = \langle 2, \overline{1, 3} \rangle$. If we set $\gamma = \langle \overline{1, 3} \rangle$, 5.41 and 5.44 show that $\beta = \langle 2, \gamma \rangle$ and that

$$\gamma = \langle 1, 3, \gamma \rangle = 1 + \cfrac{1}{3 + \cfrac{1}{\gamma}},$$

and it follows that $3\gamma^2 - 3\gamma - 1 = 0$. Since $\gamma > 0$ and this equation has only one positive root, we conclude that

$$\gamma = \frac{3 + \sqrt{21}}{6}.$$

From the equation $\beta = \langle 2, \gamma \rangle = 2 + \dfrac{1}{\gamma}$, we then find that

$$\beta = \frac{1 + \sqrt{21}}{2}.$$

In particular, we see that β is a quadratic irrationality. The following theorem, whose proof is just a generalization of the calculations which we have performed in this example, will show that this fact is not just an accident.

5.62   THEOREM. *The value of every periodic continued fraction is a quadratic irrationality.*

PROOF: Let β denote the value of the periodic continued fraction 5.61 and let $\gamma = \langle \overline{c_0, c_1, \ldots, c_{m-1}} \rangle$. Then $\gamma = \langle c_0, c_1, \ldots, c_{m-1}, \gamma \rangle$ and if the convergents of the finite continued fraction $\langle c_0, c_1, \ldots, c_{m-1} \rangle$ are denoted by $p'_k/q'_k (k = 0, 1, \ldots, m - 1)$, it follows from Theorem 5.18 that

$$\gamma = \frac{\gamma p'_{m-1} + p'_{m-2}}{\gamma q'_{m-1} + q'_{m-2}}.$$

Thus γ satisfies a quadratic equation with integral coefficients. Since γ is the value of an infinite continued fraction, γ cannot be a rational number and we conclude that γ is a quadratic irrationality. If $n = 0$, $\beta = \gamma$ and we have reached the desired conclusion. If $n > 0$, we write $\beta = \langle b_0, b_1, \ldots, b_{n-1}, \gamma \rangle$. Then, if the convergents of the continued fraction $\langle b_0, b_1, \ldots, b_{n-1} \rangle$ are denoted by p''_k/q''_k ($k = 0, 1, \ldots, n - 1$), we have

$$\beta = \frac{\gamma p''_{n-1} + p''_{n-2}}{\gamma q''_{n-1} + q''_{n-2}}.$$

Since we know that β is irrational and that γ is a quadratic irrationality, it follows that β is a quadratic irrationality. This completes the proof of the theorem.

We next change our point of view and study the infinite continued fraction expansion of a quadratic irrationality. Most of the rest of this section will be devoted to proving that such a continued fraction is necessarily periodic. This result, together with the theorem just established, shows that the real numbers which are the values of periodic continued fractions are the quadratic irrationalities and no others.

Suppose that we start with a given quadratic irrationality α. We shall use the notation introduced in Section 5.6 and denote by α_k the complete quotients in the infinite continued fraction expansion of α. As before, we shall write α_0 for α to make the notation perfectly general. Also, using the notation of Section 5.6, we let $[\alpha_k] = a_k$ and

5.63 $$\alpha_k = a_k + \frac{1}{\alpha_{k+1}}, \qquad (k = 0, 1, 2, \ldots).$$

Then

5.64 $$\alpha_0 = \langle a_0, a_1, a_2, \ldots \rangle,$$

and we wish to show that this continued fraction is necessarily periodic.

In view of Lemma 5.60, we shall take α_0 to be of the form

$$\alpha_0 = \frac{\sqrt{d} + r_0}{s_0},$$

where r_0 and s_0 are integers such that $s_0 \mid (d - r_0^2)$.

Each complete quotient α_k is a quadratic irrationality and can therefore be expressed in similar form. In order to obtain information about α_k, our procedure will be to define sequences $\{r_k\}$ and $\{s_k\}$ of rational numbers recursively, then to show that r_k and s_k are integers and that each α_k is expressible in terms of r_k and s_k in the same way that α_0 was expressed above in terms of r_0 and s_0.

Since r_0 and s_0 are given, the following equations define sequences $\{r_k\}$ and $\{s_k\}$ recursively:

5.65 $$r_{k+1} = a_k s_k - r_k, \qquad (k = 0, 1, 2, \ldots);$$

5.66 $$s_{k+1} = \frac{d - r_{k+1}^2}{s_k}, \qquad (k = 0, 1, 2, \ldots).$$

We shall now prove the following facts.

5.67   LEMMA. *For every nonnegative integer* k, *we have*

(i) r_k *and* s_k *are integers with* $s_k \neq 0$,

(ii) $s_k | (d - r_k^2)$,

(iii) $\alpha_k = \dfrac{\sqrt{d} + r_k}{s_k}$.

PROOF: All of these are true for $k = 0$. We assume their truth for k, and prove them for $k + 1$.

Clearly, 5.65 shows that r_{k+1} is an integer. Also, $s_{k+1} \neq 0$, since $d \neq r_{k+1}^2$ inasmuch as d is not a perfect square.

Next, from 5.65 and 5.66, we obtain

$$s_{k+1} = \frac{d - (a_k s_k - r_k)^2}{s_k} = \frac{d - r_k^2}{s_k} - a_k^2 s_k + 2a_k r_k.$$

By our induction hypothesis, $s_k | (d - r_k^2)$, and it follows that s_{k+1} is an integer. Then, by 5.66, we have $d - r_{k+1}^2 = s_k s_{k+1}$, so we conclude that $s_{k+1} | (d - r_{k+1}^2)$. There remains only to prove that 5.67 (iii) holds for $k + 1$.

By 5.63 and the assumption that part (iii) holds for k, we have

$$\alpha_{k+1} = \frac{1}{\alpha_k - a_k} = \frac{s_k}{\sqrt{d} + r_k - a_k s_k}$$

$$= \frac{s_k}{\sqrt{d} - r_{k+1}} \cdot \frac{\sqrt{d} + r_{k+1}}{\sqrt{d} + r_{k+1}}$$

$$= \frac{\sqrt{d} + r_{k+1}}{(d - r_{k+1}^2)/s_k} = \frac{\sqrt{d} + r_{k+1}}{s_{k+1}}.$$

This calculation establishes 5.67 (iii) with k replaced by $k + 1$, and completes the proof of the lemma by induction.

Before proceeding with the theory, let us illustrate how the continued fraction expansion of a given quadratic irrationality may be easily computed by use of the recursive relations 5.65 and 5.66.

Example 1. Find the continued fraction expansion of $\sqrt{41}$.

Solution: We have $\sqrt{41} = \dfrac{\sqrt{41} + 0}{1}$, so that $r_0 = 0$, $s_0 = 1$. Moreover, $a_0 = [\sqrt{41}] = 6$, and we have the first column of the following table.

k	0	1	2	3	4
r_k	0	6	4	6	6
s_k	1	5	5	1	5
a_k	6	2	2	12	2

To compute the second column, we calculate r_1 by use of 5.65, then s_1 by use of 5.66, and $a_1 = \left[\dfrac{\sqrt{41} + r_1}{s_1} \right]$. The remaining columns are similarly calculated in turn. Since $r_4 = r_1$ and $s_4 = s_1$, it follows that $\alpha_4 = \alpha_1$, and the calculation repeats itself. Thus we have

$$\sqrt{41} = \langle 6, \overline{2, 2, 12} \rangle.$$

From the results of Section 5.7, we know that the convergents of this continued fraction are successively better rational approximations to $\sqrt{41}$. For later use, we compute here the first few of these convergents by the procedure illustrated in Sections 5.3 and 5.4.

k	-2	-1	0	1	2	3	4	5	6
a_k			6	2	2	12	2	2	12
p_k	0	1	6	13	32	397	826	2,049	25,414
q_k	1	0	1	2	5	62	129	320	3,969

Example 2. Find the continued fraction expansion of $(\sqrt{2} + 1)/3$.

Solution: If we consider $d = 2$, $r_0 = 1$, $s_0 = 3$, it is not true that $s_0 \,|\, (d - r_0^2)$ and so we are not ready to use the recursive formulas 5.65 and 5.66. In this case, we rewrite our given quadratic irrationality as follows, using the method of proof of Lemma 5.60:

$$\frac{\sqrt{2} + 1}{3} = \frac{3\sqrt{2} + 3}{9} = \frac{\sqrt{18} + 3}{9}.$$

Now, if we set $d = 18$, $r_0 = 3$, and $s_0 = 9$, it is true that $s_0 \,|\, (d - r_0^2)$ and we can proceed to use 5.65 and 5.66. In this way, we obtain the following table.

k	0	1	2	3	4
r_k	3	-3	4	4	4
s_k	9	1	2	1	2
a_k	0	1	4	8	4

These calculations show that

$$\frac{\sqrt{2}+1}{3} = \langle 0, 1, \overline{4, 8} \rangle.$$

We again return to the general case and let α_0 be a given quadratic irrationality. The complete quotients α_k in the continued fraction expansion of $\alpha_0 = (\sqrt{d} + r_0)/s_0$ are given by Lemma 5.67 (iii). Since each α_k is a quadratic irrationality, α_k has a conjugate α_k' (as defined in the preceding section). We shall now prove another useful lemma as follows:

5.68   LEMMA. *If $n > 1$ is a positive integer such that $\alpha_{n-1}' < 0$, then*

(i) $-1 < \alpha_n' < 0,$

(ii) $0 < r_n < \sqrt{d},$

(iii) $0 < s_n < 2\sqrt{d}.$

PROOF: Since

$$\alpha_{n-1} = a_{n-1} + \frac{1}{\alpha_n},$$

it follows by taking conjugates (using 5.58) that

$$\alpha_{n-1}' = a_{n-1} + \frac{1}{\alpha_n'}.$$

Now $a_{n-1} > 0$ since $n > 1$, and we must therefore have $\alpha_n' < 0$ since $\alpha_{n-1}' < 0$. Then, using the fact that $\alpha_n' < 0$ and $\alpha_{n-1}' < 0$, we have

$$\frac{1}{\alpha_n'} = \alpha_{n-1}' - a_{n-1} < -a_{n-1} \leq -1,$$

and therefore $-1 < \alpha_n' < 0$. This establishes part (i).

Now $\alpha_n > 1$, since $n \neq 0$. Accordingly, we have

$$\alpha_n - \alpha_n' > 0 \quad \text{and} \quad \alpha_n + \alpha_n' > 0.$$

Since

$$\alpha_n = \frac{\sqrt{d} + r_n}{s_n} \quad \text{and} \quad \alpha_n' = \frac{-\sqrt{d} + r_n}{s_n},$$

we see that

$$\alpha_n - \alpha_n' = \frac{2\sqrt{d}}{s_n} > 0,$$

and $s_n > 0$. Also,

$$\alpha_n + \alpha_n' = \frac{2r_n}{s_n} > 0,$$

and $r_n > 0$. Part (ii) of the lemma now follows from the observation that

$$\alpha_n' = \frac{-\sqrt{d} + r_n}{s_n} < 0,$$

and therefore $r_n < \sqrt{d}$. Using this result and the fact that

$$\alpha_n = \frac{\sqrt{d} + r_n}{s_n} > 1,$$

we obtain $s_n < \sqrt{d} + r_n < 2\sqrt{d}$. This establishes part (iii) and completes the proof of the lemma.

It is now quite easy to prove the following principal theorem of this section.

5.69   THEROEM. *The infinite continued fraction expansion of a quadratic irrationality is periodic.*

PROOF: Let $\alpha = \alpha_0$ be a given quadratic irrationality. Using our previous notation in which the complete quotients are α_k ($k = 0, 1, 2, \ldots$), and $a_k = [\alpha_k]$, let sequences $\{p_k\}$ and $\{q_k\}$ be defined as in 5.16. Then, by 5.43, we have for each k

$$\alpha = \frac{\alpha_k p_{k-1} + p_{k-2}}{\alpha_k q_{k-1} + q_{k-2}}.$$

Taking conjugates, we have by Lemma 5.59,

$$\alpha' = \frac{\alpha_k' p_{k-1} + p_{k-2}}{\alpha_k' q_{k-1} + q_{k-2}}.$$

Solving for α_k' in terms of α, we obtain

5.70 $$\alpha_k' = -\frac{\alpha' q_{k-2} - p_{k-2}}{\alpha' q_{k-1} - p_{k-1}} = -\frac{q_{k-2}}{q_{k-1}}\left(\frac{\alpha' - p_{k-2}/q_{k-2}}{\alpha' - p_{k-1}/q_{k-1}}\right).$$

Now since $\alpha = \langle a_0, a_1, a_2, \ldots \rangle$, it follows that

$$\alpha = \lim_{k \to \infty} \frac{p_{k-2}}{q_{k-2}} = \lim_{k \to \infty} \frac{p_{k-1}}{q_{k-1}}.$$

Moreover, $\alpha \neq \alpha'$ (why?) and therefore

$$\lim_{k \to \infty} \frac{\alpha' - p_{k-2}/q_{k-2}}{\alpha' - p_{k-1}/q_{k-1}} = \frac{\alpha' - \alpha}{\alpha' - \alpha} = 1.$$

It follows from 5.70, using the fact that $q_i > 0$ for every $i \geq 0$, that $\alpha_k' < 0$ for all sufficient large values of k. Lemma 5.68 then assures us that $0 < r_k < \sqrt{d}$ and $0 < s_k < 2\sqrt{d}$ for all sufficiently large values of k. Since there are only a finite number of pairs (r_k, s_k) of positive integers which satisfy these respective inequalities, there must exist positive integers m and l such that $m < l$ with $r_m = r_l$ and $s_m = s_l$. By 5.67 (iii), it follows that $\alpha_m = \alpha_l$. This shows that the part of the continued fraction expansion of α starting with a_m coincides with the part of the expansion starting with a_l. Hence the expansion of α must be periodic, and this completes the proof of the theorem.

Exercises

1. Prove 5.58.

2. Prove Lemma 5.59.

3. Find the value of each of the following periodic continued fractions:

    (a) $\langle 3, \overline{3, 6} \rangle$,   (b) $\langle 1, \overline{2, 3} \rangle$,

    (c) $\langle 1, 2, \overline{3, 4} \rangle$,   (d) $\langle -2, \overline{1} \rangle$,

    (e) $\langle 1, 2, 3, \overline{4} \rangle$,   (f) $\langle 1, 2, 1, 2, 3, \overline{2} \rangle$.

4. If a is a positive integer, verify that

$$\langle \overline{a} \rangle = \frac{a + \sqrt{a^2 + 4}}{2}.$$

5. Find the continued fraction expansion of each of the following quadratic irrationalities, and check by calculating the value of the periodic continued fraction which you obtain:

    (a) $\sqrt{2}$,   (b) $\sqrt{3}$,   (c) $(\sqrt{3} + 2)/3$,

    (d) $\sqrt{5}$,   (e) $(1 - \sqrt{2})/2$,   (f) $\sqrt{7}$,

    (g) $\sqrt{6}$,   (h) $\dfrac{\sqrt{6} + 1}{\sqrt{6} - 1}$,   (i) $(4 + 3\sqrt{2})/2$.

6. Verify each of the following:

    (a) $\sqrt{19} = \langle 4, \overline{2, 1, 3, 1, 2, 8} \rangle$,

    (b) $\sqrt{32} = \langle 5, \overline{1, 1, 1, 10} \rangle$,

    (c) $\sqrt{43} = \langle 6, \overline{1, 1, 3, 1, 5, 1, 3, 1, 1, 12} \rangle$.

5.10   PURELY PERIODIC CONTINUED FRACTIONS

We next determine those quadratic irrationalities whose continued fraction expansions are purely periodic, that is, the period begins with the first term. First, we make the following definition.

5.71   DEFINITION. A quadratic irrationality α is said to be a *reduced* quadratic irrationality if $\alpha > 1$ and $-1 < \alpha' < 0$.

As an example, it is easy to verify that $\sqrt{3} + 1$ is a reduced quadratic irrationality.

For our purposes, the significance of this concept is indicated by the following theorem.

5.72   THEOREM. *The infinite continued fraction which represents a quadratic irrationality α is purely periodic if and only if α is a reduced quadratic irrationality.*

PROOF: Suppose, first, that $\alpha = \alpha_0$ is a reduced quadratic irrationality. Since $\alpha_0 > 1$, we have $a_0 = [\alpha_0] \geq 1$. Then, since $\alpha_0' < 0$, the equation

$$\alpha_0' = a_0 + \frac{1}{\alpha_1'}$$

shows that $\alpha_1' < 0$. From Lemma 5.68 we see that $-1 < \alpha_k' < 0$ for *every* nonnegative integer k. In general, we have

$$\alpha_k' = a_k + \frac{1}{\alpha_{k+1}'},$$

or

$$-\frac{1}{\alpha_{k+1}'} = a_k - \alpha_k'.$$

Since $-1 < \alpha_k' < 0$, we conclude that

5.73
$$a_k = \left[-\frac{1}{\alpha_{k+1}'} \right].$$

We shall presently make use of this fact.

In the periodic continued fraction expansion of α_0, let n be the smallest nonnegative integer such that the complete quotient α_n occurs again, and let m be a positive integer such that $\alpha_n = \alpha_{n+m}$. Let us now assume that $n > 0$ and seek a contradiction. Since $\alpha_n = \alpha_{n+m}$, we have $\alpha_n' = \alpha_{n+m}'$, and therefore

$$\left[-\frac{1}{\alpha_n'} \right] = \left[-\frac{1}{\alpha_{n+m}'} \right].$$

In view of 5.73, we conclude that $a_{n-1} = a_{n+m-1}$. Hence we have

$$\alpha_{n+m-1} = a_{n-1} + \frac{1}{\alpha_{n+m}}.$$

However,

$$\alpha_{n-1} = a_{n-1} + \frac{1}{\alpha_n} = a_{n-1} + \frac{1}{\alpha_{n+m}},$$

and we see that $\alpha_{n-1} = \alpha_{(n-1)+m}$ and therefore α_{n-1} occurs again. This contradicts our choice of n, and we conclude that we must have $n = 0$. Accordingly, the continued fraction representation of α is purely periodic.

Conversely, suppose that

$$\alpha = \langle a_0, a_1, \ldots, a_{m-1} \rangle$$

is a purely periodic continued fraction. Since $a_0 = a_m$ and $m > 0$, we must have $a_0 \geq 1$ and therefore $\alpha > 1$. Of course, $m \geq 1$ and it is clear that $\alpha_m = \alpha_0 = \alpha$. By 5.43, we have

$$\alpha = \frac{\alpha p_{m-1} + p_{m-2}}{\alpha q_{m-1} + q_{m-2}},$$

from which it follows that

$$q_{m-1}\alpha^2 + (q_{m-2} - p_{m-1})\alpha - p_{m-2} = 0.$$

If we set $f(x) = q_{m-1}x^2 + (q_{m-2} - p_{m-1})x - p_{m-2}$, we have just verified that $f(\alpha) = 0$. By results of Section 5.8, we know that the other root of the quadratic equation $f(x) = 0$ is α'. Since $a_k > 0$ for every nonnegative integer k, Definition 5.16 shows that for $k \geq -1$, $\{p_k\}$ is a strictly increasing sequence, except that we may have $p_0 = p_{-1}$. Similarly, for $k \geq -1$, $\{q_k\}$ is a strictly increasing sequence, except that we may have $q_1 = q_0$. Hence

$$f(-1) = (q_{m-1} - q_{m-2}) + (p_{m-1} - p_{m-2}) > 0.$$

Since $f(0) < 0$, the equation $f(x) = 0$ must have a real root between -1 and 0. However, $\alpha > 1$ and we conclude that the root α' must be such that $-1 < \alpha' < 0$. This shows that α is a reduced quadratic irrationality, and completes the proof of the theorem.

As an example, we pointed out above that $\sqrt{3} + 1$ is a reduced quadratic irrationality. In view of the theorem just established, the continued fraction expansion of $\sqrt{3} + 1$ must be purely periodic. We leave it to the reader to verify that $\sqrt{3} + 1 = \langle \overline{2, 1} \rangle$.

5.11 THE CONTINUED FRACTION EXPANSION OF $\sqrt{d}$

It is now easy to obtain some information about the continued fraction expansion of $\sqrt{d}$, where d is a positive integer which is not a perfect square. We first establish the following result.

5.74   THEOREM. *If d is a positive integer which is not a perfect square, the continued fraction expansion of $\sqrt{d}$ has a period which begins after exactly one term, that is, it is of the form*

5.75 $$\sqrt{d} = \langle a_0, \overline{a_1, a_2, \ldots, a_m} \rangle$$

for some positive integer m.

PROOF: We now have the special case in which $\alpha_0 = \sqrt{d} > 1$. Moreover, it is clear that α_0 is not a reduced quadratic irrationality, since $\alpha_0' = -\sqrt{d} < -1$, and Theorem 5.72 shows that the continued fraction expansion of $\sqrt{d}$ is not purely periodic. However, since

$$\alpha_0 = a_0 + \frac{1}{\alpha_1},$$

we have

$$\alpha_1 = \frac{1}{\sqrt{d} - a_0}, \quad \alpha_1' = \frac{1}{-\sqrt{d} - a_0},$$

and since $a_0 \geq 1$, it follows easily that α_1 is reduced. Hence, by the preceding theorem, the continued fraction expansion of α_1 is purely periodic and $\sqrt{d}$ necessarily has an expansion of the form 5.75. The proof is therefore completed.

Although we shall not here give a proof of this interesting fact, it is true that in the expansion 5.75 of $\sqrt{d}$ the last term a_m of a period is always equal to $2a_0$.

We shall next prove the following result in which we let $\alpha_0 = \sqrt{d}$ and use the notation introduced in Section 5.9.

5.76   THEOREM. *Let d be a positive integer which is not a perfect square. For the continued fraction expansion 5.75 of $\sqrt{d}$ with period of length m, we have the following:*

(i) $p_{k-1}^2 - dq_{k-1}^2 = (-1)^k s_k,$ $(k = 0, 1, 2, \ldots).$

(ii) $s_k > 0,$ $(k = 0, 1, 2, \ldots).$

(iii) $s_k = 1$ if and only if $m \mid k.$

PROOF: For each nonnegative integer k, we have

$$\alpha_0 = \sqrt{d} = \frac{\alpha_k p_{k-1} + p_{k-2}}{\alpha_k q_{k-1} + q_{k-2}}.$$

By 5.67 (iii), we know that

$$\alpha_k = \frac{\sqrt{d} + r_k}{s_k},$$

and if we substitute this expression for α_k in the preceding equation, we obtain

$$\sqrt{d} = \frac{(\sqrt{d} + r_k)p_{k-1} + s_k p_{k-2}}{(\sqrt{d} + r_k)q_{k-1} + s_k q_{k-2}},$$

which can be written in the form

$$\sqrt{d}(r_k q_{k-1} + s_k q_{k-2} - p_{k-1}) + dq_{k-1} - r_k p_{k-1} - s_k p_{k-2} = 0.$$

This equation now implies the truth of both of the following equations:

$$r_k q_{k-1} + s_k q_{k-2} = p_{k-1},$$

$$r_k p_{k-1} + s_k p_{k-2} = dq_{k-1}.$$

If we multiply the first of these equations by p_{k-1} and the second by $-q_{k-1}$ and add the resulting equations, we obtain

$$s_k(p_{k-1}q_{k-2} - p_{k-2}q_{k-1}) = p_{k-1}^2 - dq_{k-1}^2.$$

Theorem 5.21 then shows that

$$s_k(-1)^k = p_{k-1}^2 - dq_{k-1}^2,$$

and the proof of part (i) is completed.

Since $\alpha = \sqrt{d}$, we have $r_0 = 0$, $s_0 = 1$. In particular $s_0 > 0$. If $k > 0$, $c_{k-1} = p_{k-1}/q_{k-1}$ is a convergent in the continued fraction expansion of $\sqrt{d}$. Moreover, since $a_0 = [\sqrt{d}] > 0$, we have $p_{k-1} > 0$ and $q_{k-1} > 0$. It follows from Theorem 5.30 that $p_{k-1}^2 - dq_{k-1}^2$ is positive or negative according as k is even or odd. Part (ii) of the present theorem is then an immediate consequence of part (i). It is also true that $r_k > 0$ for $k > 0$, but we shall not need this fact and so we shall not prove it here.

Since $r_0 = 0$ and $s_0 = 1$, 5.65 and 5.66 show that $r_1 = a_0$, $s_1 = d - a_0^2$. In the periodic continued fraction 5.75, we have $\alpha_{tm+1} = \alpha_1$ for each positive integer t. Thus, by 5.67 (iii), we can conclude that $r_{tm+1} = a_0$, $s_{tm+1} = d - a_0^2$. Again using 5.66 (with $k = tm$), we obtain

$$d - a_0^2 = s_{tm}(d - a_0^2),$$

and we conclude that $s_{tm} = 1$. This establishes one part of (iii). Suppose, now, that k is a positive integer such that $s_k = 1$. Thus we have $\alpha_k = \sqrt{d} + r_k$ and $[\alpha_k] = [\sqrt{d}] + r_k = a_0 + r_k$. It follows that

$$\alpha_k = \sqrt{d} + r_k = (a_0 + r_k) + \frac{1}{\alpha_{k+1}},$$

or

$$\sqrt{d} = a_0 + \frac{1}{\alpha_{k+1}}.$$

This implies that $\alpha_{k+1} = \alpha_1$ and therefore that a_k is the last term in a period. That is, we must have $k = tm$ for some positive integer t. The proof of the theorem is therefore completed.

5.12 THE EQUATION $x^2 - dy^2 = 1$

We shall conclude our discussion of continued fractions by applying some of our results to the problem of obtaining all solutions in integers of an equation of the form

5.77 $$x^2 - dy^2 = 1,$$

in which d is a positive integer which is not a perfect square. In the literature this equation is usually referred to as Pell's equation.

If x_0 and y_0 are integers such that $x_0^2 - dy_0^2 = 1$, we shall refer to the pair (x_0, y_0) as a solution of Equation 5.77. If both x_0 and y_0 are positive integers, we may call (x_0, y_0) a positive solution. Clearly, $(\pm 1, 0)$ is a solution; and if (x_0, y_0) is a solution, so also is $(\pm x_0, \pm y_0)$. Without loss of generality, we shall henceforth be primarily interested in positive solutions.

Since $\sqrt{d} > 1$, in the continued fraction expansion 5.75 of $\sqrt{d}$ we must have $a_0 > 0$. Accordingly, the corresponding p_k and q_k are positive for all $k \geq 0$. From Theorem 5.76, we can now establish the following result.

5.78 Theorem. *Let p_k/q_k be the convergents in the continued fraction 5.75 which represents $\sqrt{d}$, and let m be the length of the period.*

(a) *If m is even, (p_i, q_i) is a solution of Equation 5.77 if and only if $i = tm - 1$ for some positive integer t.*

(b) *If m is odd, (p_i, q_i) is a solution of Equation 5.77 if and only if $i = 2tm - 1$ for some positive integer t.*

Proof: By Theorem 5.76 (with $k - 1$ replaced by i), if $i \geq 0$ we see that (p_i, q_i) is a positive solution of Equation 5.77 if and only if $(-1)^{i+1} = 1$ and $m \mid (i + 1)$. If m is even, these conditions are satisfied if and only if $i = tm - 1$ for some positive integer t. If m is odd, they are satisfied if and only if $i = 2tm - 1$ for some positive integer t. This completes the proof of the theorem.

In particular, this theorem establishes the interesting fact that *every* equation of the form $x^2 - dy^2 = 1$, in which d is a positive integer which is not a perfect square, has an infinite number of solutions in integers.

This theorem specifies those convergents to the continued fraction expansion of $\sqrt{d}$ which yield solutions of our equation 5.77. The next theorem shows that there are no other solutions.

5.79 Theorem. *If p and q are positive integers such that $p^2 - dq^2 = 1$, then p/q is a convergent in the continued fraction expansion of $\sqrt{d}$.*

Proof: We have $(p - q\sqrt{d})(p + q\sqrt{d}) = 1$, from which it follows that

$$\frac{p}{q} - \sqrt{d} = \frac{1}{q(p + q\sqrt{d})} > 0.$$

Since $p^2 = 1 + dq^2$, we have $p > q$ and therefore $p + q\sqrt{d} > 2q$. Hence

$$0 < \frac{p}{q} - \sqrt{d} < \frac{1}{2q^2},$$

and the desired conclusion is an immediate consequence of Theorem 5.50.

We now know that *every* positive solution of Equation 5.77 is of the form (p_i, q_i) with i restricted as in Theorem 5.78. If (x_0, y_0) and (x_1, y_1) are positive solutions of Equation 5.77, then $x_0 < x_1$ if and only if $y_0 < y_1$. The smallest positive solution, that is, the positive solution (x_0, y_0) with the property that $x_0 < x_1$ and $y_0 < y_1$ for every other positive solution (x_1, y_1) is called the *fundamental solution*. Since the sequences $\{p_k\}$ and $\{q_k\}$ are positive and strictly increasing, the following result is an immediate consequence of the two preceding theorems.

5.80 COROLLARY. *Let m be the length of the period in the continued fraction expansion of $\sqrt{d}$. Then the fundamental solution of Equation 5.77 is (p_{m-1}, q_{m-1}) if m is even, and is (p_{2m-1}, q_{2m-1}) if m is odd.*

Example 1. Determine the fundamental solution of the equation $x^2 - 41y^2 = 1$.

Solution: The continued fraction expansion of $\sqrt{41}$ was obtained in Example 1 of Section 5.9, and several convergents were computed. It was found that $\sqrt{41} = \langle 6, \overline{2, 2, 12} \rangle$ so that $m = 3$. By the preceding corollary, the fundamental solution is (p_5, q_5), which is $(2049, 320)$.

Example 2. Determine the fundamental solution of the equation $x^2 - 23y^2 = 1$.

Solution: The continued fraction expansion of $\sqrt{23}$ is given by the following calculations.

k	0	1	2	3	4	5
r_k	0	4	3	3	4	4
s_k	1	7	2	7	1	7
a_k	4	1	3	1	8	1

k	-2	-1	0	1	2	3
a_k			4	1	3	1
p_k	0	1	4	5	19	24
q_k	1	0	1	1	4	5

The first table shows that $\sqrt{23} = \langle 4, \overline{1, 3, 1, 8} \rangle$, so that $m = 4$. By Corollary 5.80, the desired fundamental solution is (p_3, q_3), and the second table shows that this fundamental solution is $(24, 5)$.

In both these examples (and in general), additional solutions may be obtained by computing additional convergents and making use of Theorem 5.78. However, we shall now present an easier way to obtain additional solutions after the fundamental solution has been obtained.

Our calculations will be in the field $R(\sqrt{d})$, as introduced in Section 5.8. First, let us prove the following lemma.

5.81   LEMMA. *Let* (u_1, v_1) *and* (u_2, v_2) *be arbitrary (not necessarily positive) solutions of Equation 5.77. If integers* u_3 *and* v_3 *are defined by*

$$(u_1 + v_1\sqrt{d})(u_2 + v_2\sqrt{d}) = u_3 + v_3\sqrt{d},$$

then (u_3, v_3) *also is a solution of this equation.*

PROOF: Straightforward calculations show that $u_3 = u_1u_2 + v_1v_2d$, $v_3 = u_1v_2 + u_2v_1$, and that

$$u_3^2 - dv_3^2 = (u_1u_2 + v_1v_2d)^2 - d(u_1v_2 + u_2v_1)^2$$
$$= (u_1^2 - dv_1^2)(u_2^2 - dv_2^2) = 1.$$

Now suppose that (x_0, y_0) is the fundamental solution of Equation 5.77. By applying the lemma, we see that if for each positive integer n, we define (x_n, y_n) by the equation

5.82 $$(x_0 + y_0\sqrt{d})^n = x_n + y_n\sqrt{d},$$

then (x_n, y_n) is a positive solution of Equation 5.77. The following result shows that *all* positive solutions can be obtained in this way.

5.83   THEOREM. *If* (x_0, y_0) *is the fundamental solution of Equation 5.77 and if integers* x_n *and* y_n *are defined by Equation 5.82, then*

$$(x_n, y_n), \qquad\qquad (n = 1, 2, \dots),$$

are all the positive solutions of Equation 5.77.

PROOF: Let us set $\gamma = x_0 + y_0\sqrt{d}$ and let (u, v) be an arbitrary positive solution of Equation 5.77. Since $\gamma > 1$, γ^n becomes arbitrarily large for large n. Moreover, the fact that (x_0, y_0) is the fundamental solution assures us that $\gamma \le u + v\sqrt{d}$. Hence there exists a positive integer n such that

$$\gamma^n \le u + v\sqrt{d} < \gamma^{n+1}.$$

Since $x_0^2 - dy_0^2 = (x_0 + y_0\sqrt{d})(x_0 - y_0\sqrt{d}) = 1$, we thus obtain

5.84 $$1 \le (u + v\sqrt{d})\,\gamma^{-n} = (u + v\sqrt{d})(x_0 - y_0\sqrt{d})^n < \gamma.$$

If we define u_1 and v_1 by the equation

5.85 $$(u + v\sqrt{d})(x_0 - y_0\sqrt{d})^n = u_1 + v_1\sqrt{d},$$

the preceding lemma shows that (u_1, v_1) is a solution of Equation 5.77 and we have

5.86 $$1 \le u_1 + v_1\sqrt{d} < \gamma.$$

Since $u_1^2 - dv_1^2 = 1$, clearly $u_1 \ne 0$. We are going to prove that $v_1 = 0$. Let us assume, on the contrary, that $v_1 \ne 0$ (so that both u_1 and v_1 are nonzero integers) and seek a contradiction. Inequality 5.86 shows that u_1 and v_1 cannot both be negative. Moreover, the equation

$$(u_1 + v_1\sqrt{d})(u_1 - v_1\sqrt{d}) = 1,$$

together with 5.86 shows that

$$0 < u_1 - v_1\sqrt{d} \le 1,$$

and we cannot have one of u_1, v_1 positive and the other negative. We conclude that both u_1 and v_1 are positive, and (u_1, v_1) is therefore a positive solution of Equation 5.77. However, this contradicts 5.86 since (x_0, y_0) is the fundamental solution and $\gamma = x_0 + y_0\sqrt{d} \le u_1 + v_1\sqrt{d}$. We conclude that $v_1 = 0$, and it follows that $u_1 = \pm 1$. Actually, 5.86 shows that $u_1 = 1$ and we have $u_1 + v_1\sqrt{d} = 1$. It follows from 5.85 and 5.84 that

$$(u + v\sqrt{d})\,\gamma^{-n} = 1,$$

that is, that

$$u + v\sqrt{d} = \gamma^n.$$

Thus $(u, v) = (x_n, y_n)$, and the proof of the theorem is completed.

As an example, we showed above that the fundamental solution of the equation $x^2 - 23y^2 = 1$ is $(24, 5)$. This theorem shows that all positive solutions are of the form (x_n, y_n), where

$$(24 + 5\sqrt{23})^n = x_n + y_n\sqrt{23}, \quad (n = 1, 2, \dots).$$

In particular, it is easily verified that

$$(24 + 5\sqrt{23})^2 = 1151 + 240\sqrt{23},$$

and we conclude that (1151, 240) not only is a solution but that it is the next largest solution. That is, there is no positive solution (u, v) of this equation with $24 < u < 1151$.

Exercises

1. Verify by inspection that $(10, 3)$ is the fundamental solution of the equation $x^2 - 11y^2 = 1$. Find three other solutions by use of Lemma 5.81.

    For each of the equations of Exercises 2–7, apply Corollary 5.80 to verify that the given solution is the fundamental solution.

2. $x^2 - 13y^2 = 1$,   (649, 180).
3. $x^2 - 21y^2 = 1$,   (55, 12).
4. $x^2 - 29y^2 = 1$,   (9801, 1820).
5. $x^2 - 31y^2 = 1$,   (1520, 273).
6. $x^2 - 37y^2 = 1$,   (73, 12).
7. $x^2 - 45y^2 = 1$,   (161, 24).

8. If p and q are positive integers such that $p^2 - dq^2 = -1$, where d is a positive integer which is not a perfect square, prove that p/q is a convergent in the continued fraction expansion of $\sqrt{d}$. [*Hints:* Cf. proof of Theorem 5.79. Show that

$$0 < \sqrt{d} - \frac{p}{q} = \frac{1}{q(p + q\sqrt{d})}.$$

Then show that $p \geq q$.]

9. Use the preceding exercise and Theorem 5.76 to prove that the equation $x^2 - dy^2 = -1$ has no solution (in integers) if the length m of the period in the continued fraction expansion of $\sqrt{d}$ is even; and that if m is odd, every positive solution is of the form (p_i, q_i) for $i = tm - 1$ with t *odd*.

10. Use your calculations for Exercises 2–7 to determine whether each of the following equations has a solution; and if it has a solution, find the smallest positive solution:

    (a) $x^2 - 13y^2 = -1$,   (b) $x^2 - 21y^2 = -1$,
    (c) $x^2 - 29y^2 = -1$,   (d) $x^2 - 31y^2 = -1$.
    (e) $x^2 - 37y^2 = -1$,   (f) $x^2 - 45y^2 = -1$.

Additional Topics

1. Pell's equation and generalizations. Nagell, Chap. 6; Gelfond, Secs. 4 and 5; LeVeque [10], Vol. 1, Chap. 8.

2. More about approximation by rational numbers. Niven and Zuckerman, p. 148; Rademacher, Chap. 6.

3. A geometric interpretation of continued fractions. Davenport, p. 111.

REFERENCES

1. Carmichael, R. D. *The Theory of Numbers*. New York: John Wiley & Sons, 1914.
2. Davenport, H. *The Higher Arithmetic*. London: Hutchinson's University Library, 1952.
3. Dickson, L. E. *History of the Theory of Numbers*. Washington: Carnegie Institution, Vol. 1, 1919; Vol. 2, 1920; Vol. 3, 1923. (Reprinted by Chelsea Publishing Co., New York.)
4. Dickson, L. E. *Introduction to the Theory of Numbers*. Chicago: University of Chicago Press, 1929.
5. Gelfond, A. O. *The Solution of Equations in Integers*. San Francisco: W. H. Freeman and Co., 1961. (Translated from the Russian by J. B. Roberts.)
6. Griffin, Harriet. *Elementary Theory of Numbers*. New York: McGraw-Hill Book Co., 1954.
7. Hardy, G. H., and E. M. Wright. *An Introduction to the Theory of Numbers*, third edition. Oxford: Clarenden Press, 1954.

143

8. Jones, B. W. *The Theory of Numbers*. New York: Holt, Rinehart & Winston, 1955.

9. Landau, E. *Elementary Number Theory*. New York: Chelsea Publishing Co., 1958. (Translated from the German by Jacob E. Goodman.)

10. LeVeque, W. J. *Topics in Number Theory*. 2 vols. Reading, Mass.: Addison-Wesley Publishing Co., 1956.

11. LeVeque, W. J. *Elementary Theory of Numbers*. Reading, Mass.: Addison-Wesley Publishing Co., 1962.

12. Nagell, T. *Introduction to Number Theory*. New York: John Wiley & Sons, 1951.

13. Niven, I., and H. S. Zuckerman. *An Introduction to the Theory of Numbers*. New York: John Wiley & Sons, 1960.

14. Ore, Oystein. *Number Theory and its History*. New York: McGraw-Hill Book Co., 1948.

15. Rademacher, Hans. *Lectures on Elementary Number Theory*. New York: Blaisdell Publishing Co., 1964.

16. Shanks, Daniel. *Solved and Unsolved Problems in Number Theory*. Washington, D.C.: Spartan Books, 1962.

17. Stewart, B. M. *Theory of Numbers*, second edition. New York: The Macmillan Co., 1964.

18. Uspensky, J. V., and M. A. Heaslet. *Elementary Number Theory*. New York: McGraw-Hill Book Co., 1939.

19. Vinogradov, I. M. *An Introduction to the Theory of Numbers*. New York: Pergamon Press, 1955. (Translated from the sixth Russian edition by Helen Popova.)

20. Wright, H. N. *First Course in Theory of Numbers*. New York: John Wiley & Sons, 1939.

TABLE 1

Primes less than 1000 and their least primitive roots.

p	g	p	g	p	g	p	g	p	g	p	g
2	1	127	3	283	3	467	2	661	2	877	2
3	2	131	2	293	2	479	13	673	5	881	3
5	2	137	3	307	5	487	3	677	2	883	2
7	3	139	2	311	17	491	2	683	5	887	5
11	2	149	2	313	10	499	7	691	3	907	2
13	2	151	6	317	2	503	5	701	2	911	17
17	3	157	5	331	3	509	2	709	2	919	7
19	2	163	2	337	10	521	3	719	11	929	3
23	5	167	5	347	2	523	2	727	5	937	5
29	2	173	2	349	2	541	2	733	6	941	2
31	3	179	2	353	3	547	2	739	3	947	2
37	2	181	2	359	7	557	2	743	5	953	3
41	6	191	19	367	6	563	2	751	3	967	5
43	3	193	5	373	2	569	3	757	2	971	6
47	5	197	2	379	2	571	3	761	6	977	3
53	2	199	3	383	5	577	5	769	11	983	5
59	2	211	2	389	2	587	2	773	2	991	6
61	2	223	3	397	5	593	3	787	2	997	7
67	2	227	2	401	3	599	7	797	2		
71	7	229	6	409	21	601	7	809	3		
73	5	233	3	419	2	607	3	811	3		
79	3	239	7	421	2	613	2	821	2		
83	2	241	7	431	7	617	3	823	3		
89	3	251	6	433	5	619	2	827	2		
97	5	257	3	439	15	631	3	829	2		
101	2	263	5	443	2	641	3	839	11		
103	5	269	2	449	3	643	11	853	2		
107	2	271	6	457	13	647	5	857	3		
109	6	277	5	461	2	653	2	859	2		
113	3	281	3	463	3	659	2	863	5		

TABLE 2

Ind a for odd moduli $q < 50$.

a \ q	3	5	7	9	11	13	17	19	23	25	q / a
1	0	0	0	0	0	0	0	0	0	0	1
2	1	1	2	1	1	1	14	1	2	1	2
3		3	1		8	4	1	13	16	7	3
4		2	4	2	2	2	12	2	4	2	4
5			5	5	4	9	5	16	1		5
6			3		9	5	15	14	18	8	6
7				4	7	11	11	6	19	5	7
8				3	3	3	10	3	6	3	8
9					6	8	2	8	10	14	9
10					5	10	3	17	3		10
11						7	7	12	9	16	11
12						6	13	15	20	9	12
13							4	5	14	19	13
14							9	7	21	6	14
15							6	11	17		15
16							8	4	8	4	16
17								10	7	13	17
18								9	12	15	18
19									15	18	19
20									5		20
21									13	12	21
22									11	17	22
23										11	23
24										10	24

TABLE 2—continued)

q / a	27	29	31	37	41	43	47	49	q / a
1	0	0	0	0	0	0	0	0	1
2	1	1	24	1	26	27	18	26	2
3		5	1	26	15	1	20	1	3
4	2	2	18	2	12	12	36	10	4
5	5	22	20	23	22	25	1	29	5
6		6	25	27	1	28	38	27	6
7	16	12	28	32	39	35	32		7
8	3	3	12	3	38	39	8	36	8
9		10	2	16	30	2	40	2	9
10	6	23	14	24	8	10	19	13	10
11	13	25	23	30	3	30	7	40	11
12		7	19	28	27	13	10	11	12
13	8	18	11	11	31	32	11	33	13
14	17	13	22	33	25	20	4		14
15		27	21	13	37	26	21	30	15
16	4	4	6	4	24	24	26	20	16
17	15	21	7	7	33	38	16	25	17
18		11	26	17	16	29	12	28	18
19	12	9	4	35	9	19	45	35	19
20	7	24	8	25	34	37	37	39	20
21		17	29	22	14	36	6		21
22	14	26	17	31	29	15	25	24	22
23	11	20	27	15	36	16	5	38	23
24		8	13	29	13	40	28	37	24
25	10	16	10	10	4	8	2	16	25
26	9	19	5	12	17	17	29	17	26
27		15	3	6	5	3	14	3	27
28		14	16	34	11	5	22		28
29			9	21	7	41	35	18	29
30			15	14	23	11	39	14	30
31				9	28	34	3	7	31
32				5	10	9	44	4	32
33				20	18	31	27	41	33
34				8	19	23	34	9	34
35				19	21	18	33		35
36				18	2	14	30	12	36
37					32	7	42	32	37
38					35	4	17	19	38
39					6	33	31	34	49
40					20	22	9	23	40
41						6	15	15	41
42						21	24		42
43							13	6	43
44							43	8	44
45							41	31	45
46							23	22	46
47								5	47
48								21	48

Index